Revision Notes for Higher Mathematics

Andrew Sinclair

Depute Head Teacher
Mearns Castle High School

Editorial assistance by

Eileen Young

Depute Head Teacher

Bearsden Academy

Published by
Chemcord
Inch Keith
East Kilbride
Glasgow

ISBN 1 870570 71 5

First Reprint 2003

Printed by Bell and Bain Ltd, Glasgow

About This Book

This book covers all you need to know for **Higher Mathematics**. The content is arranged to match the three **National Units**, **Mathematics 1**, **Mathematics 2** and **Mathematics 3** which together make up the **National Course** in **Mathematics** at the **Higher level**.

It does **not** cover **Statistics (H)**, the optional unit which can be taken instead of Mathematics 3.

Each of the three units covers four main **topic areas** from the Higher syllabus. In this book, a separate chapter has been allocated to each topic area. Each chapter has been further divided into sections to make it easier for you to find the particular topics you require.
All sections have been numbered, eg

	1.3.6	unit **1**	**Mathematics 1**
1.3.6	1.3.6	topic area **3**	**Basic Differentiation**
	1.3.6	section **6**	**Using the Derivative**

An extra chapter, labelled **0**, has been added which covers some general background topics which you should know.

All key results are 'boxed' and key terms are shown **in bold like this** so that you can find them quickly. Additional comments to help you understand the examples are given ***in bold italics like this***.

The **Contents Summary** on pages 2 and 3 give the general outline of the book and a summary of the topics covered. A **Detailed Index** has been added on pages 140 to 142 to help you find particular topics or terms easily.

The book can be used:

as a reference book - when you come across a term or topic that you are unsure about, look up that topic area in the book and refresh your memory, but make sure you understand it properly when you do. Keep the book for reference if you intend to study maths after Higher level.

to revise a particular topic - read through the material carefully. Make sure that you know all formulae and standard results. Study the examples given so that you understand how they are worked out. Then try some more examples on the topic from your textbook or jotters.

alongside past papers - in the final lead-up to your exams, the best revision is to work through exam papers from previous years. When you come across a question that you are unable to answer, look up that topic area in the book and see if a similar example is given. With over 200 examples in the book, there is a good chance of finding something that will help.

CONTENTS SUMMARY

2 MATHEMATICS 2

3 MATHEMATICS 3

0 SYMBOLS, TERMS AND SETS

The topics in this section are used throughout the course and should be known. They will not be examined formally in themselves.

0.1 Set Notation

In mathematics, a collection of items, often numbers, is called a **set**.
It can be written as a list inside **curly brackets**,
eg the set of vowels, V, can be written as V = {a, e, i, o, u},
the set of letters of the alphabet, L, can be written as L = {a, b, c, ..., z}.

Each item is called a **member** or **element** of the set.
You write $\mathbf{a} \in \mathbf{V}$ to mean "a is an element of the set V", and $\mathbf{b} \notin \mathbf{V}$ to mean "b is not an element of the set V".
A set with no members is called the **empty set**, and written **{ }**.

If all the members, or elements, of a set V are also members of another set L, you say that V is a **subset** of L, and write it $\mathbf{V} \subset \mathbf{L}$,
eg the set of vowels V is a subset of the set of all letters L.

0.2 Types of Numbers

Most of the work in Higher Grade uses the following sets of numbers:

Natural numbers $\mathbf{N} = \{ 1, 2, 3, 4, 5, ... \}$

Whole numbers $\mathbf{W} = \{ 0, 1, 2, 3, 4, ... \}$

Integers $\mathbf{Z} = \{ ..., -3, -2, -1, 0, 1, 2, 3, ... \}$

Rational numbers $\mathbf{Q} = \left\{ \frac{a}{b} \text{ where } a \text{ and } b \text{ are integers} \right\}$

ie any number that can be written in the form of a fraction

Irrational numbers eg $\sqrt{2}$, $\sqrt[3]{5}$, π, e, etc

Real numbers $\mathbf{R} = \{$ all rational and irrational numbers $\}$

Assume that you are using real numbers unless you are told otherwise.

Sometimes the context of a question will make a restriction on the type of answer, eg non-negative, non-fraction.

0.3 Intervals

A subset of the set of real numbers is called an **interval**.

If both end points of the interval are included, it is called a **closed interval**, eg $-2 \le x \le 4$. This can be written as $[-2, 4]$, using square brackets.

If either end point of the interval is not included, it is called an **open interval**, eg $-2 < x < 4$. This can be written as $(-2, 4)$, using round brackets.

Intervals can also be written using set notation, eg $\{x : x > 2, x \in \mathbf{R}\}$ means "the set of all real numbers greater than 2".

0.4 Exact Values

For many practical applications of maths, it is sufficient to obtain a numerical value to a required degree of accuracy as a solution. In this case, it is often a rounded-off value obtained from a calculator. This is called an **approximate value**.

In some mathematical problems, you are required to obtain an **exact value** for the solution.

When finding exact values, you must leave all fractions as common fractions, and simplify your solutions as far as possible. You must not use numerical approximations for surds, trig ratios or constants like π.

Example: If $\pi x^2 = 2$, find the exact value of x, and the approximate value correct to 2 decimal places.

$$\pi x^2 = 2$$

$$x^2 = \frac{2}{\pi}$$

$$x = \sqrt{\frac{2}{\pi}}$$ ◄—— $\sqrt{\frac{2}{\pi}}$ is the exact value of x.

$$= \sqrt{\frac{2}{3.14...}}$$

$$= 0.797...$$ ◄—— **0.80** is the approximate value of x, correct to 2 dp.

1.1 PROPERTIES OF THE STRAIGHT LINE

1.1.1 The Gradient of a Line

The **gradient** of a line is a number which measures the steepness of the slope. It is given by:

$$m = \frac{y}{x} = \frac{vertical}{horizontal}$$

The gradient of the line joining $A\ (x_1, y_1)$ to $B\ (x_2, y_2)$ is given by:

$$m_{AB} = \frac{y_2 - y_1}{x_2 - x_1} \qquad x_1 \neq x_2$$

Lines with a **positive** gradient slope **up** to the right.

Lines with a **negative** gradient slope **down** the right.

The larger the number "value", ie the more positive or the more negative, the steeper the line.

The gradient of a **vertical** line is said to be **undefined**.

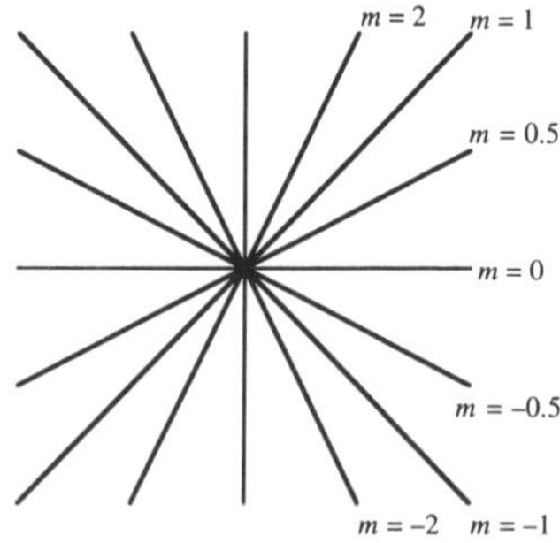

The gradient of a **horizontal** line will be **zero**.

1.1.2 Gradients and Angles

The angle, θ, that a line makes with the positive direction of the x-axis is related to the gradient of the line, m, by the formula:

$$m = \tan\theta$$

The angle, θ, is measured anti-clockwise. The scales on each axis must be the same.

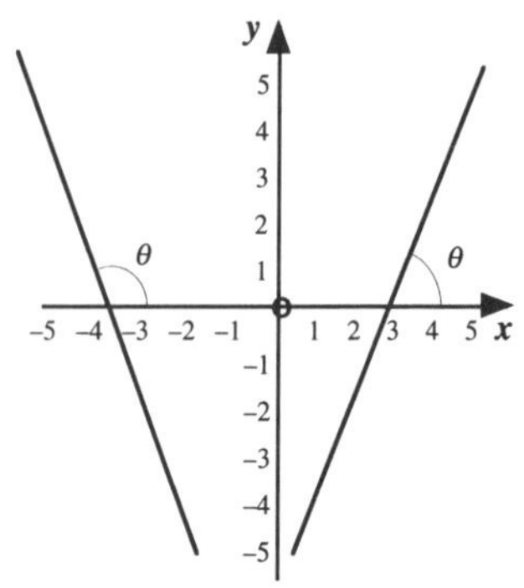

Example: What angle does the line through P $(10,5)$ and Q $(4,-3)$ make with the positive direction of the x-axis?

$$
\begin{aligned}
m_{PQ} &= \frac{y_2 - y_1}{x_2 - x_1} \\
&= \frac{-3-5}{4-10} \\
&= \frac{-8}{-6} \\
&= \tfrac{4}{3}
\end{aligned}
$$

$m_{PQ} = \tan\theta$

$\tan\theta = \tfrac{4}{3}$

tangent is positive in 1st Quadrant

$$
\begin{aligned}
RA &= \tan^{-1}\left(\tfrac{4}{3}\right) \\
&= 53.13...
\end{aligned}
$$

$\theta = \mathbf{53.1^\circ}$ to 1 dp

Note: A negative gradient will lead to a 2nd Quadrant angle.

1.1.3 Parallel and Perpendicular Lines

Two lines with gradients m_1 and m_2 are **parallel** if and only if:

$$\boxed{\boldsymbol{m_1 = m_2}}$$

Two lines with gradients m_1 and m_2 are **perpendicular** if and only if:

$$\boxed{\boldsymbol{m_1 m_2 = -1}}$$

1.1.4 The Equation of a Straight Line $y = mx + c$

> When the equation of a straight line is written in the form
>
> $y = mx + c,$
>
> the value $\boldsymbol{m}$ gives the **gradient** of the line,
> and the value $\boldsymbol{c}$ gives the **y-axis intercept** $(\mathbf{0},\boldsymbol{c})$.

This is the most useful and easiest to use form of the equation of a straight line as it allows you to easily identify the gradient and y-axis intercept.

Example 1: Find the equation of the line cutting the y-axis at $(0,5)$ perpendicular to the line with equation $2x + 3y = 6$.

First rearrange the equation into the $y = mx + c$ form to find the gradient of the given line, then use it to obtain the gradient of the other line.

$$2x+3y=6$$
$$3y=-2x+6$$
$$y=\frac{-2}{3}x+\frac{6}{3}$$
$$y=-\tfrac{2}{3}x+2$$
$$m_1=-\tfrac{2}{3}$$

$$m_1m_2=-1$$
$$-\tfrac{2}{3}\times m_2=-1$$
$$m_2=\tfrac{3}{2}$$

$$y=mx+c$$
$$\mathbf{y=\tfrac{3}{2}x+5}$$

The $y = mx + c$ form also allows a very quick method of sketching a straight line.

1. Rearrange the equation into $y = mx + c$ form.
2. Mark the y-axis intercept on the diagram.
3. Use the gradient to find a series of other points on the line,

eg for a gradient of $\frac{y}{x}$, go x horizontally to the right, and y vertically, **up** if the gradient is **positive**, and **down** if the gradient is **negative**.

Example 2: Sketch the line with equation $2x + 3y = 9$.

$$2x+3y=9$$
$$3y=-2x+9$$
$$y=-\tfrac{2}{3}x+3$$
$$m=-\tfrac{2}{3},\quad c=3.$$

Plot the y-axis intercept $(0,3)$.

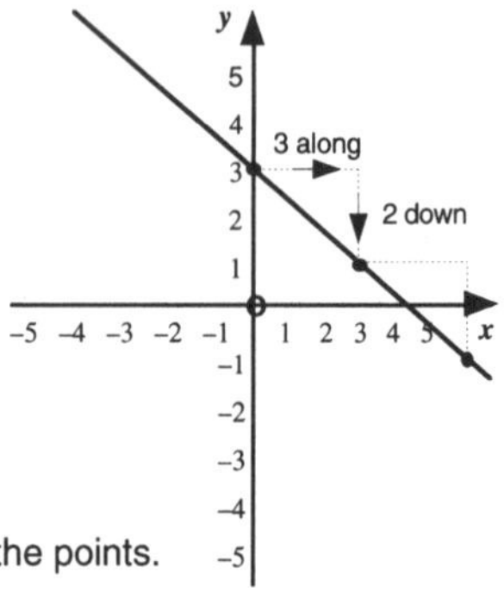

$m=\frac{y}{x}=\frac{-2}{3}$ ie 3 along and 2 down

Go 3 along, down 2 and plot $(3,1)$.

Plot another point and draw a line through the points.

1.1.5 The Linear Form of the Equation of a Straight Line

> Every straight line has an equation which can be given in the form
>
> $$ax + by + c = 0$$
>
> (a, b and c are integers, and a and b are not both zero)
>
> and every equation of this form will give a straight line.

The equations for horizontal and vertical lines are special cases of this result when either a or b is zero.

A **vertical** line has an equation of the form:

$$\boxed{x = c}$$

A **horizontal** line has an equation of the form:

$$\boxed{y = d}$$

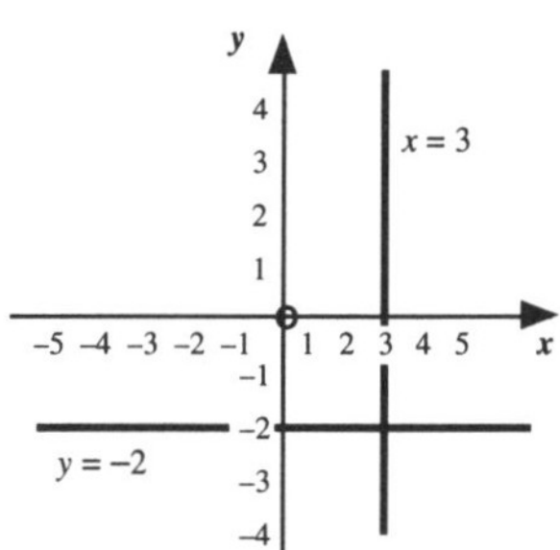

1.1.6 Finding the Equation of a Straight Line

You can find the equation of a straight line using the following formula, if you know, or can find, the gradient and any point on the line:

> $m = ???$ $\qquad$ $(a,b) = ???$
>
> $$y - b = m(x - a)$$
>
> where m is the gradient and (a,b) is any point on the line

In practice, it may help you to set out the formula as above and then check off the gradient and the point when you obtain each.

Once you have found the equation, you have a choice of forms to leave it in. Unless the question specifies a particular form, either the standard form $y = mx + c$ or the "simultaneous equation" form $ax + by = c$ is the most useful.

Example: Find the equation of the line through (2,–3) parallel to the line with equation $x - 3y = 9$.

First find the gradient of the given line, then use it to get the gradient of the other line. Substitute the gradient and the point into the formula.

$$x - 3y = 9$$
$$x - 9 = 3y$$
$$y = \frac{1}{3}x - \frac{9}{3}$$
$$y = \tfrac{1}{3}x - 3$$
$$m_1 = \tfrac{1}{3}$$
$$m_2 = \tfrac{1}{3}$$

$m = \tfrac{1}{3}$ ✔ $(a,b) = (2,-3)$ ✔

$$y - b = m(x - a)$$
$$y - (-3) = \tfrac{1}{3}(x - 2)$$
$$3y + 9 = x - 2$$
$$\mathbf{x - 3y = 11}$$

1.1.7 The Midpoint of the Line AB

The midpoint, M_{AB}, of the line AB is given by:

$$M_{AB} = \left(\frac{x_1 + x_2}{2}, \frac{y_1 + y_2}{2}\right)$$

1.1.8 The Distance Formula

The distance, d_{AB}, between points A and B is given by:

$$d_{AB} = \sqrt{(x_2 - x_1)^2 + (y_2 - y_1)^2}$$

Example: Find the distance between A (–4,3) and B (3,–2).

$$d_{AB} = \sqrt{(x_2 - x_1)^2 + (y_2 - y_1)^2}$$
$$= \sqrt{(3 - (-4))^2 + (-2 - 3)^2}$$
$$= \sqrt{(7)^2 + (-5)^2}$$
$$= \sqrt{49 + 25} = \sqrt{74}$$

AB is **8.6 units** to 1dp.

1.1.9 Collinear Points

Three or more points are said to be **collinear** if they lie on the same straight line.

To prove three points A, B and C are collinear, you can use gradients, but it is simpler to use vectors (see Section 3.1.6).
Exam questions involving collinearity have always made use of vectors.

1.1.10 Concurrent Lines

Three or more lines are said to be **concurrent** if they intersect at the same point.

1.1.11 Special Lines in a Triangle

A line from the midpoint of a side to the opposite vertex is called a **median**.

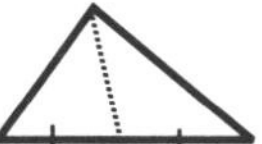

A line from a vertex which meets the opposite side at right angles is called an **altitude**.
It is used to give the **perpendicular height** of a triangle.

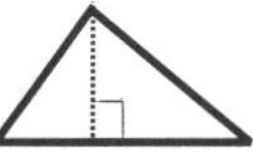

A line which passes through the midpoint of a side at right angles to the side is called a **perpendicular bisector**.

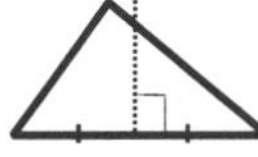

A line which bisects an angle of a triangle is called an **angle bisector**.

The three medians in any triangle are concurrent (see Example 1 in the next section).

Similarly, the altitudes are concurrent, the perpendicular bisectors are concurrent and the angle bisectors are concurrent.

1.1.12 Intersection of Two Straight Lines

When two lines meet, they **intersect** each other.

If the first line cuts the second line in half, it **bisects** it. If they each cut the other in half they **bisect each other**.

You use the methods of **simultaneous equations** to find an intersection point.

To show that more than two lines are concurrent, use simultaneous equations once to find the intersection point. It is then quicker to substitute that point into any other equation to show the line passes through it (see Example 1 below).

Example 1: ABC is an isosceles triangle with coordinates (2,2), (6,2) and (4,8) respectively.
Find the point where the median through A meets the median through B, and show that all the medians of triangle ABC are concurrent.

Make a sketch to help you see what is being asked. Use your sketch to check answers, but do not read answers from the diagram.

Introduce letters for any other points you use. Use headings and labels to make it clear what you are doing.

Find the equation of each median.

Use simultaneous equations to find the intersection point of one pair, and then check whether that point also lies on the the third median.

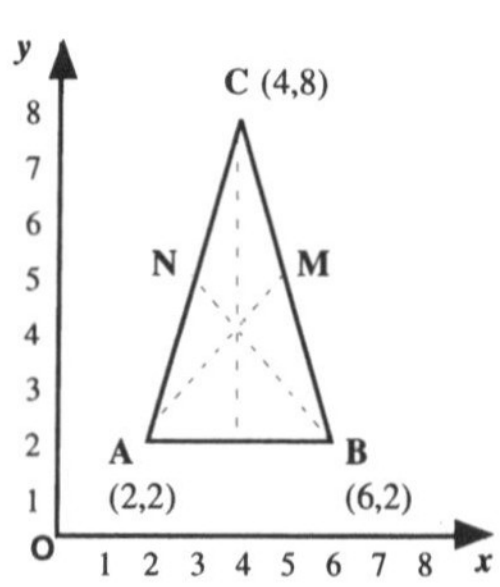

Median through A:

$$M_{BC} = \left(\frac{x_1 + x_2}{2}, \frac{y_1 + y_2}{2}\right) = \left(\frac{6+4}{2}, \frac{2+8}{2}\right) = (5,5)$$

$$m_{AM} = \frac{y_2 - y_1}{x_2 - x_1} = \frac{5-2}{5-2} = \frac{3}{3} = 1$$

$m = 1$ ✔ $\quad (a,b) = (2,2)$ ✔

$$y - b = m(x - a)$$
$$y - 2 = 1(x - 2)$$
$$y - 2 = x - 2$$
$$x - y = 0$$

Median through B:

$$N_{AC}=\left(\frac{x_1+x_2}{2},\frac{y_1+y_2}{2}\right) \qquad m_{BN}=\frac{y_2-y_1}{x_2-x_1} \qquad m=-1 \qquad (a,b)=(6,2)$$

$$=\left(\frac{2+4}{2},\frac{2+8}{2}\right) \qquad =\frac{5-2}{3-6}$$

$$=(3,5) \qquad =\frac{3}{-3}$$

$$=-1$$

$$y-b=m(x-a)$$
$$y-2=-1(x-6)$$
$$y-2=-x+6$$
$$x+y=8$$

Intersection point of medians:

$x-y=0$ Equation (1)

$x+y=8$ Equation (2)

Adding

$2x=8$

$x=4$

Substitute 4 for x into Equation (2)

$4+y=8$

$y=4$

The medians through A and B intersect at (4,4).

Median through C:

Midpoint of AB = (4,2)

Since AB is horizontal, the median will be a vertical line.

Median through C $\quad x=4$

(4,4) also lies on $x=4$, the median through C.

So **the medians are concurrent.**

Example 2: PQR is the triangle with coordinates (–5,1), (10, –2) and (7,9) respectively.
The perpendicular bisector of PR meets the altitude through R at K.
Find the coordinates of K.

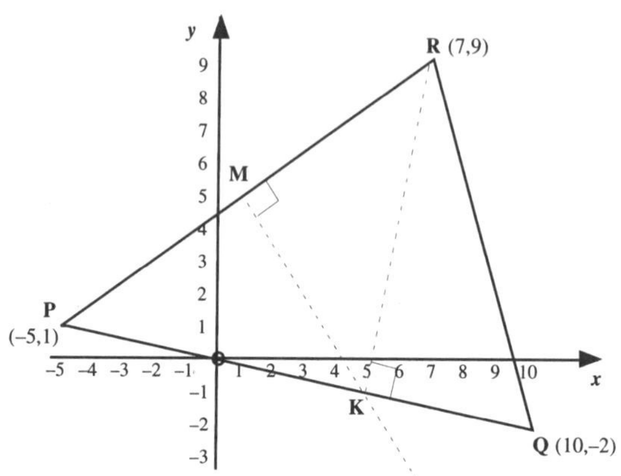

Perpendicular bisector of PR:

$$M_{PR} = \left(\frac{x_1 + x_2}{2}, \frac{y_1 + y_2}{2}\right) = \left(\frac{-5+7}{2}, \frac{1+9}{2}\right) = (1,5)$$

$$m_{PR} = \frac{y_2 - y_1}{x_2 - x_1} = \frac{9-1}{7-(-5)} = \frac{8}{12} = \tfrac{2}{3}$$

$$m_1 m_2 = -1$$
$$\tfrac{2}{3} \times m_2 = -1$$
$$m_2 = -\tfrac{3}{2}$$

✔ $m = -\tfrac{3}{2}$ ✔ $(a,b) = (1,5)$

$$y - b = m(x-a)$$
$$y - 5 = -\tfrac{3}{2}(x-1)$$
$$2y - 10 = -3x + 3$$
$$3x + 2y = 13$$

Altitude through R:

$$m_{PQ} = \frac{y_2 - y_1}{x_2 - x_1} = \frac{-2-1}{10-(-5)} = \frac{-3}{15} = -\tfrac{1}{5}$$

$$m_1 m_2 = -1$$
$$-\tfrac{1}{5} \times m_2 = -1$$
$$m_2 = 5$$

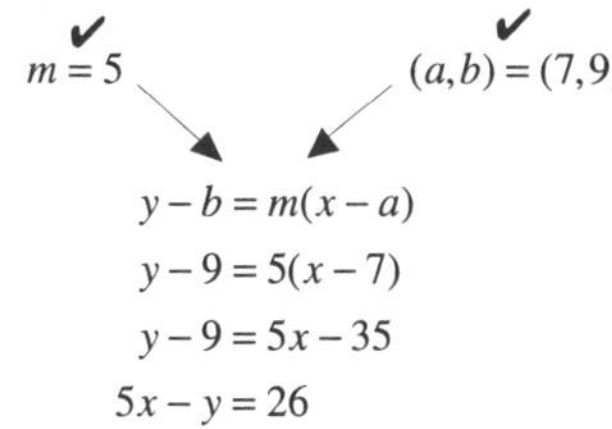

$$y - b = m(x - a)$$
$$y - 9 = 5(x - 7)$$
$$y - 9 = 5x - 35$$
$$5x - y = 26$$

Intersection point of lines:

$3x + 2y = 13$ Equation $(\mathbf{1})$

$5x - y = 26$ Equation $(\mathbf{2})$

$(\mathbf{1})$ $3x + 2y = 13$

$(\mathbf{2}) \times 2$ $10x - 2y = 52$

Adding $13x = 65$

$x = 5$

Substitute 5 for x into Equation $(\mathbf{2})$

$$5 \times 5 - y = 26$$
$$25 - 26 = y$$
$$y = -1$$

K = $(\mathbf{5}, \mathbf{-1})$

1.2 FUNCTIONS AND GRAPHS

1.2.1 Function Definitions and Notation

A **function** is a mathematical rule which inputs values, acts on them and outputs corresponding values.

For each input value x, the corresponding output value $f(x)$ is called the **image of x under f**. The set of all input values x is called the **domain** of the function. The set of all images for that domain is called the **range** of the function.

To qualify as a function, a rule must meet the following condition:
each member of the domain must have exactly one image under the function.

A rule would fail to qualify as a function if, for example, it attempted to divide by zero or to take the square root of a negative number for some of the input values,

eg $f(x) = \frac{1}{x}$ when $x = 0$, $g(x) = \sqrt{x}$ when $x = -2$.

In cases like these, it is still possible to obtain a function by **restricting the domain** - removing any "problem" values.

For $f(x) = \frac{1}{x}$ the largest possible domain would be the set of all real numbers except $x = 0$. You can write this as $\{x : x \neq 0, x \in \mathbf{R}\}$.

For $g(x) = \sqrt{x}$ the largest possible domain is $\{x : x \geq 0, x \in \mathbf{R}\}$.

Some mathematical rules output more than one value for a particular input value,

eg $g(x) = \sqrt{x}$ when $x = 4$, $g(4) = \sqrt{4} = 2$ or -2,

$h(x) = \sin^{-1} x$ when $x = 0.5$, $h(0.5) = \sin^{-1} 0.5 = 30°,\ 150°,\ 390°, \ldots$.

In cases like these, you can **restrict the definition of the rule**,

eg define the square root to give the positive value only,
define the inverse sine function to produce one particular value.

Example: What is the largest domain for which the following would be functions?

(a) $f(x) = \frac{3}{x-2}$ (b) $g(x) = \sqrt{x-5}$ (c) $h(x) = x^2 - 5$

(a) Problem when $x - 2 = 0$ $x = 2$

Largest domain is $\{\boldsymbol{x} : \boldsymbol{x} \neq \mathbf{2}, \boldsymbol{x} \in \mathbf{R}\}$.

(b) Problem when $x-5<0 \quad x<5$

Largest domain is $\{\boldsymbol{x : x \geq 5, x \in \mathbf{R}}\}$.

Problem of two values for $\sqrt{\ }$

$g(x)$ is defined to be the positive value of the square root.

(c) No problem values

$h(x)$ is defined for all real numbers, $\mathbf{R}$.

1.2.2 Composition of Functions

When a function f acts on a function value $g(x)$ you call this a **composite function** and write it $\boldsymbol{f(g(x))}$. The formula for $f(g(x))$ can be found by substituting the formula for $g(x)$ in place of x in the formula for $f(x)$.

Example 1: Find the formulae for $f(g(x))$ and $g(f(x))$ where

$f(x)=x^2-3$ and $g(x)=2x-3$.

$$\begin{aligned} f(g(x)) &= (2x-3)^2-3 \\ &= (4x^2-12x+9)-3 \\ &= \mathbf{4x^2-12x+6} \end{aligned}$$

$$\begin{aligned} g(f(x)) &= 2(x^2-3)-3 \\ &= 2x^2-6-3 \\ &= \mathbf{2x^2-9} \end{aligned}$$

Example 2: Find the formula for $f(g(x))$ and state the values of x for which $f(g(x))$ would not be defined, where

$f(x)=\dfrac{3}{x^2-1}$ and $g(x)=x-3$.

$$\begin{aligned} f(g(x)) &= \frac{3}{(x-3)^2-1} \\ &= \frac{3}{x^2-6x+9-1} \\ &= \frac{\mathbf{3}}{\mathbf{x^2-6x+8}} \end{aligned}$$

problem when $x^2-6x+8=0$

$(x-4)(x-2)=0$

$x-4=0$ or $x-2=0$

$x=4$ or $x=2$

$f(g(x))$ is not defined when $\boldsymbol{x=2}$ or $\boldsymbol{x=4}$.

1.2.3 Inverse Functions

Some functions can be "undone" by a corresponding rule which maps y back onto x. To qualify as a function, this rule must also meet the condition stated in Section 1.2.1. In this case you call it the **inverse function** of $f(x)$ and write it as $f^{-1}(x)$.

You will use the idea of an inverse function in Section 1.2.20 and Section 3.3.1 to introduce the logarithmic functions as inverses of exponential functions.

In the Higher exam, you will not be asked to find the formula for an inverse of a function.

1.2.4 Common Functions

You should be familiar with some of the common types of functions and their graphs - simple polynomials like linear and quadratic, trigonometric, exponential and logarithmic functions.

You must be able to sketch their graphs and recognise the functions from their graphs.

1.2.5 Linear Functions

Any function whose equation has the form $f(x) = ax + b$ is called a **linear function**.

The graph of any linear function will be a straight line.

Methods for sketching linear functions are covered in Section 1.1.4, as for $y = mx + c$.

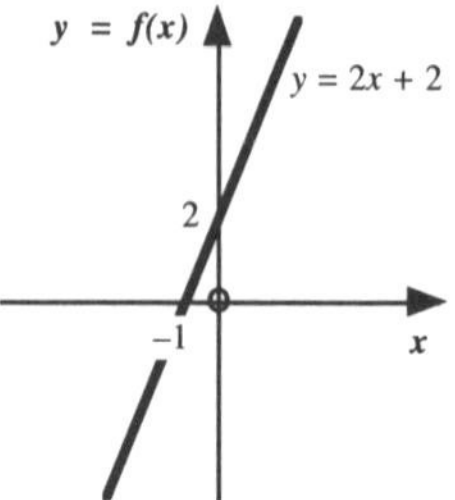

1.2.6 Quadratic Functions

Any function of the form $f(x) = ax^2 + bx + c \quad (a \neq 0)$ is called a **quadratic function**. You have already met quadratic functions in the Standard Grade course.

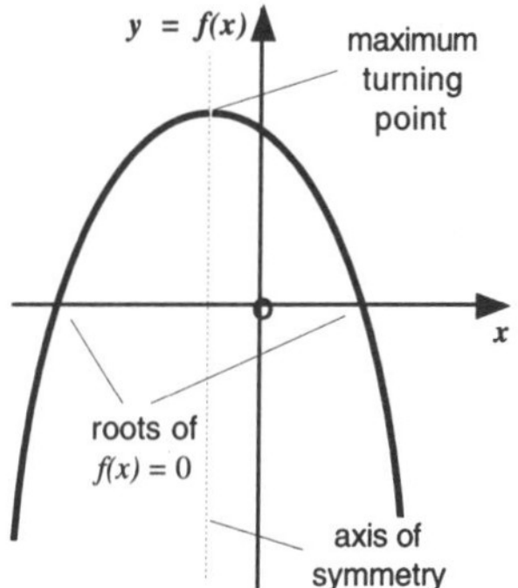

The graph of any quadratic function will be a **parabola**.

Every parabola is a symmetric curve, with a vertical **axis of symmetry**.

The parabola can sit U-shaped or upside down U-shaped.

The points where the parabola cuts the x-axis are called the **roots**.

1.2.7 The Completed Square Form of $x^2 + bx + c$

When a quadratic expression of the form $x^2 + bx + c$ is changed into the form of a square term plus a constant, ie $(x + p)^2 + q$ or $(x - p)^2 + q$, you are **completing the square**.

To find the completed square form, you must add an appropriate constant to the x^2 and x terms to create a perfect square form $(x + p)^2$ or $(x - p)^2$.
p will always be half of b and the required constant will be p^2.
The expression must then be balanced by subtracting p^2 outside the bracket.

Example 1:

$$\begin{aligned} x^2 + 6x - 3 &= (x^2 + 6x + \underline{\quad}) - 3 - \underline{\quad} \\ &= (x^2 + 6x + \underline{3^2}) - 3 - \underline{3^2} \\ &= \mathbf{(x+3)^2 - 12} \end{aligned}$$

Example 2:

$$\begin{aligned} x^2 - 4x + 13 &= (x^2 - 4x + \underline{\quad}) + 13 - \underline{\quad} \\ &= (x^2 - 4x + \underline{2^2}) + 13 - \underline{2^2} \\ &= \mathbf{(x-2)^2 + 9} \end{aligned}$$

Example 3:

$$\begin{aligned} x^2 - 3x + 1 &= (x^2 - 3x + \underline{\quad}) + 1 - \underline{\quad} \\ &= (x^2 - 3x + \underline{\left(\tfrac{3}{2}\right)^2}) + 1 - \underline{\left(\tfrac{3}{2}\right)^2} \\ &= (x - \tfrac{3}{2})^2 + \tfrac{4}{4} - \tfrac{9}{4} \\ &= \mathbf{(x - \tfrac{3}{2})^2 - \tfrac{5}{4}} \end{aligned}$$

1.2.8 The Completed Square Form of $ax^2 + bx + c$

A quadratic expression of the form $ax^2 + bx + c$ is changed in a similar way into a completed square form $a(x + p)^2 + q$ or $a(x - p)^2 + q$. Extra care must be taken in balancing the terms, particularly if a is negative.

Example 1:

$$2x^2 + 12x - 3$$
$$= (2x^2 + 12x + \_\ ) - 3 - \_$$
$$= 2(x^2 + 6x + \_\ ) - 3 - \_$$
$$= 2(x^2 + 6x + \underline{3^2}) - 3 - \underline{2 \times 3^2}$$
$$= \mathbf{2(x + 3)^2 - 21}$$

The term added on inside the bracket, 3^2, is being multiplied by the 2 outside the bracket. You must balance this therefore by subtracting **2×3^2**.

Example 2:

$$5 + 16x - x^2$$
$$= -(x^2 - 16x + \_\ ) + 5 - \_$$
$$= -(x^2 - 16x + \underline{8^2}) + 5 - \underline{(-1) \times 8^2}$$
$$= -(x - 8)^2 + 69$$
$$= \mathbf{69 - (x - 8)^2}$$

1.2.9 Using the Completed Square Form of $ax^2 + bx + c$

The completed square form allows you to identify the maximum or minimum value of a quadratic expression and where it occurs, without using calculus.

$a(x + p)^2 + q$ **has a minimum value of** q **when** $x = -p$	$(a > 0)$
$q - a(x + p)^2$ **has a maximum value of** q **when** $x = -p$	

The completed square form can then be used to find maximum / minimum values of more complex functions (see the Example below), or to find the turning point when making a sketch of a quadratic function (see Example 1 in Section 1.2.10).

Example: Find the minimum value of the function $\dfrac{1}{9-8x-x^2}$.

$$\begin{aligned} 9-8x-x^2 &= -(x^2+8x+\underline{\ \ }) + 9 - \underline{\ \ } \\ &= -(x^2+8x+\underline{4^2}) + 9 - \underline{(-1)\times 4^2} \\ &= -(x+4)^2 + 25 \\ &= 25-(x+4)^2 \end{aligned}$$

$9-8x-x^2$ has maximum value of 25.

$\dfrac{1}{9-8x-x^2}$ has minimum value of $\frac{1}{25}$.

1.2.10 Sketching Quadratics

A rough sketch of a parabola can be obtained by either method shown below.

Example 1 illustrates the use of the completed square method. This will give the coordinates of the turning point but not the intercepts.

If the x-axis intercepts are required, use the method shown in Example 2. You should still give the coordinates of the turning point (see Example 2).

It is helpful to note that a **positive x^2 term** will give a **U-shape**, and a **negative x^2 term** will give an **upside down U-shape**.

Example 1: Find the minimum value of x^2-2x-6, and hence sketch the graph of $y = x^2-2x-6$, showing clearly the minimum turning point.

$$\begin{aligned} x^2-2x-6 &= (x^2-2x+\underline{\ \ }) - 6 - \underline{\ \ } \\ &= (x^2-2x+\underline{1^2}) - 6 - \underline{1^2} \\ &= (x-1)^2 - 7 \end{aligned}$$

x^2-2x-6 has a minimum value of **−7** when $x-1=0$, ie $\boldsymbol{x = 1}$.

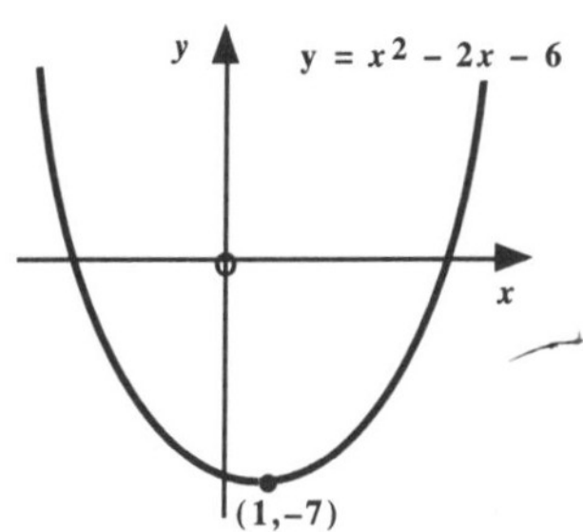

Example 2: Sketch the the graph of the function $f(x) = x^2 - 3x$.

x-axis intercepts:

Solve $f(x) = 0$

$$x^2 - 3x = 0$$

$$x(x-3) = 0$$

$$x = 0 \quad \text{or} \quad x - 3 = 0$$

$$x = 3$$

The x-axis intercepts are $(0,0)$ and $(3,0)$.

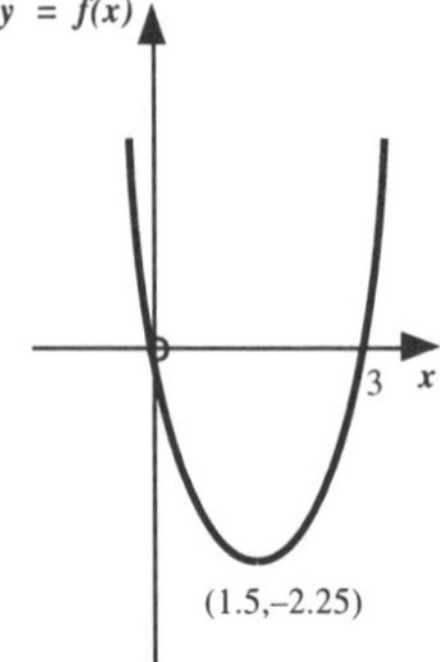

Turning point:

Because of the symmetry of the parabola, the turning point is midway between the roots.

$x = 1.5 \quad y = 1.5^2 - 3 \times 1.5 = -2.25$

The turning point is $(1.5, -2.25)$.

y-axis intercept:

$x = 0 \quad y = 0^2 - 3 \times 0 = 0$ The y-axis intercept is $(0,0)$.

1.2.11 Finding a Quadratic Formula from a Graph

Every quadratic graph will have a general equation of the form $y = ax^2 + bx + c$.

If you know any three points on the graph, you could use simultaneous equations to find the formula. The y-axis intercept will always be $(0,c)$ which can reduce the work involved. However the following approach will usually still be quicker.

If the graph cuts the x-axis at a, then $(x - a)$ must be a factor of the formula. It is helpful to remember and use the standard forms shown below.

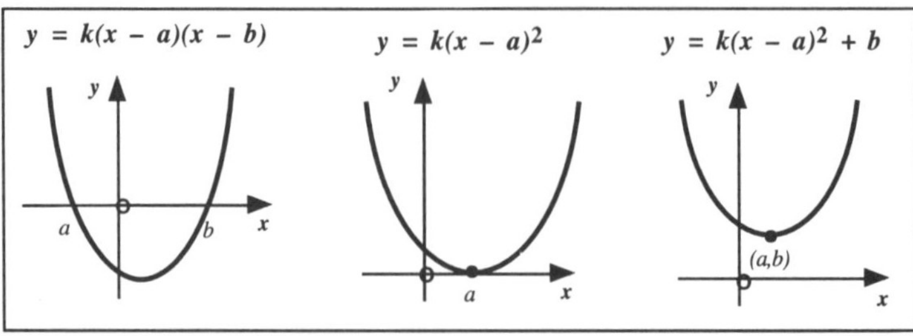

The k value in each case can be found by checking one other point, if possible the y-axis intercept. If the parabola is a U-shape, then k will be positive. If the parabola is an upside down U-shape, then k will be negative.

Example: The sketch shows the graph of a quadratic function. Find its equation.

The x-axis intercepts are $(-2,0)$ and $(4,0)$, so the formula will have general form

$$y = k(x-a)(x-b)$$
$$= k(x-(-2))(x-4)$$
$$= k(x+2)(x-4)$$

The y-axis intercept is $(0,16)$ so

$$16 = k(0+2)(0-4)$$
$$16 = -8k$$
$$k = \frac{16}{-8} = -2$$

The quadratic has equation $\mathbf{y = -2(x+2)(x-4).}$

1.2.12 Polynomial Functions

To draw a graph of a polynomial function of degree greater than 2 (see Section 2.1.1), you would normally use the curve sketching methods from Section 1.3.10 involving calculus.

A polynomial of degree n will contain a maximum of $n-1$ turning points.

You should be familiar with the shape of a general **cubic** function (degree 3),

$$f(x) = ax^3 + bx^2 + cx + d,$$

and **quartic** function (degree 4),

$$f(x) = ax^4 + bx^3 + cx^2 + dx + e.$$

The shape of the basic cubic $y = x^3$ is shown below broken, and a general cubic shape is shown solid. Similarly for the quartic.

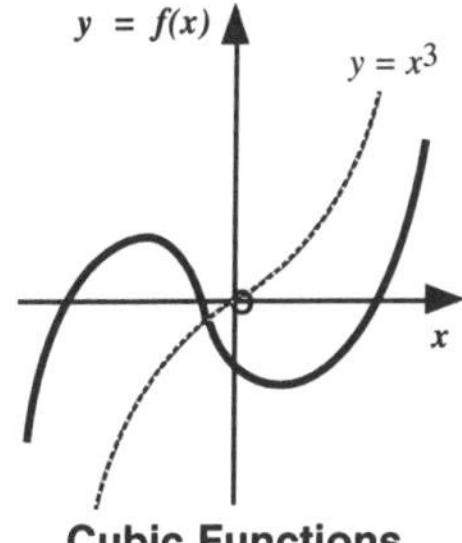

Cubic Functions

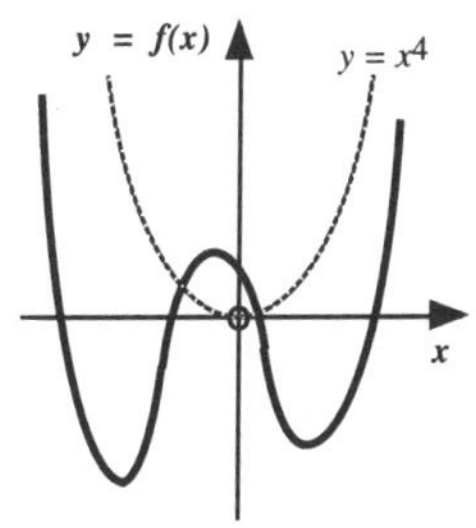

Quartic Functions

1.2.13 Trigonometric Functions

Any function of the form $f(x) = a\sin(bx + c) + d$ or $f(x) = a\cos(bx + c) + d$ is called a **trigonometric function**.

All trigonometric graphs of this type are wave-shaped and **periodic**, ie they repeat their basic pattern continuously along the length of the graph.

Each basic pattern is called a **cycle**, and the length of a cycle is called the **period** of the graph. The height of the wave above the centre line (shown broken below) is called the **amplitude** of the wave.

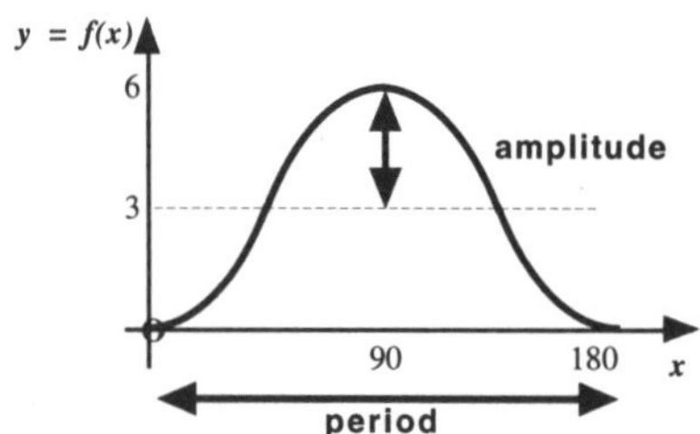

1.2.14 Sketching Trigonometric Functions: $f(x) = a\sin bx + c$ (or cos)

In Standard Grade, you learned how to sketch trig functions of the form $f(x) = a\sin bx + c$ or $f(x) = a\cos bx + c$ using degrees.

In functions of these types,
- the a value (ignoring any negative sign) gives the amplitude, (a negative a value has the effect of turning the basic shape upside down)
- the b value gives the number of complete cycles between 0° and 360°, and
- the c value gives the amount by which the centre line has shifted - if c is **positive** it will have shifted **up**, if c is **negative** it will have shifted **down**.

Example 1: Give the equation of the curve for the example shown in Section 1.2.13 above.

The basic shape is an upside down cosine, and the amplitude is 3.
The period is 180°, so there are 2 cycles between 0° and 360°.
The centre line has been raised by 3.

$a = -3 \qquad b = 2 \qquad c = 3$

The curve has equation $\mathbf{y = -3\cos 2x° + 3}$.

Example 2: Sketch the graph of $y = 4\sin 3x^\circ - 2$ for $0 \leq x \leq 360$.

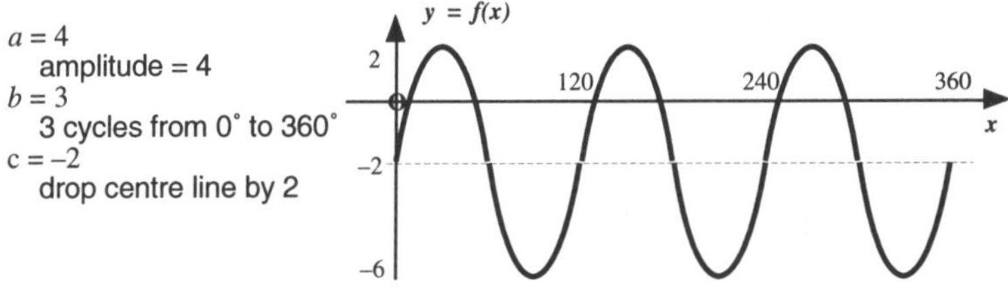

1.2.15 Radian Measure

Angles can be measured in radians as well as degrees.

A radian is defined to be the angle at the centre of a circle corresponding to an arc with length equal to the radius.

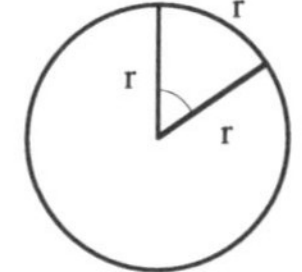

1 radian is approximately 57.3°.
It is more useful to remember the following relationship.

π **radians = 180°**

A few special angles can be given in radians as exact multiples and fractions of π. You should remember these.

$0^\circ = 0$	$30^\circ = \frac{\pi}{6}$	$45^\circ = \frac{\pi}{4}$	$60^\circ = \frac{\pi}{3}$
$90^\circ = \frac{\pi}{2}$	$180^\circ = \pi$	$270^\circ = \frac{3\pi}{2}$	$360^\circ = 2\pi$

The exact radian values of other special angles can be found from these, eg

$$135^\circ = 90^\circ + 45^\circ = \frac{\pi}{2} + \frac{\pi}{4} = \frac{3\pi}{4} \text{ radians}$$

If necessary, you can convert any angle from one unit to the other as follows.

$$65^\circ = \frac{65}{180} \times \pi = 1.13\ldots \text{ radians} \qquad 2.5 \text{ radians} = \frac{2.5}{\pi} \times 180 = 143.2\ldots^\circ$$

1.2.16 The Exact Values of the Trig Ratios for the Special Angles

The sine, cosine and tangent ratios for these special angles can also be given as exact values. These should be known, both for degrees and radians, and must be used if an exact value is required.

degrees	0°	30°	45°	60°	90°
radians	0	$\frac{\pi}{6}$	$\frac{\pi}{4}$	$\frac{\pi}{3}$	$\frac{\pi}{2}$
sin	0	$\frac{1}{2}$	$\frac{1}{\sqrt{2}}$	$\frac{\sqrt{3}}{2}$	1
cos	1	$\frac{\sqrt{3}}{2}$	$\frac{1}{\sqrt{2}}$	$\frac{1}{2}$	0
tan	0	$\frac{1}{\sqrt{3}}$	1	$\sqrt{3}$	∞

The tangent of 90° is said to be **undefined**.

The other values can be obtained by using simple trig in the two triangles opposite. One is an isosceles triangle and the other is half of an equilateral triangle.

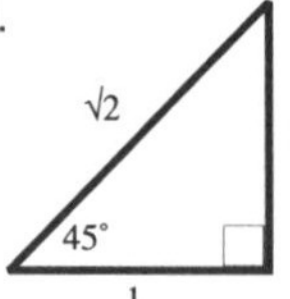

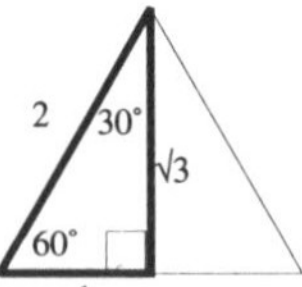

1.2.17 Sketching Trigonometric Functions: $f(x) = a\sin(bx + c) + d$ (or cos)

In Higher Maths, you must also be able to sketch graphs of functions which use radians. You use exactly the same methods as for degrees.

You also will meet functions with a constant term c added to the variable. This has the effect of a horizontal shift of the curve to the right or left (see Section 1.2.21).

When $b = 1$, the curve will shift horizontally by c to the left when $c > 0$, or to the right when $c < 0$. See Example 1.

When $b \neq 1$, you must be more careful when considering the shift.

The shift in this case is $\frac{c}{b}$ since $bx + c = b\left(x + \frac{c}{b}\right)$.

It is easier to check where the sine or cosine cycle begins by solving $bx + c = 0$. This will give the x value that acts as zero in the sine or cosine function.

Example 1: Sketch the curve $y = \sin(x - \frac{\pi}{2})$ for $0 \le x \le 2\pi$.

$x - \frac{\pi}{2} = 0$

$x = \frac{\pi}{2}$

The graph will be a sine curve starting at $\frac{\pi}{2}$*,*

ie a shift of $\frac{\pi}{2}$ *to the right.*

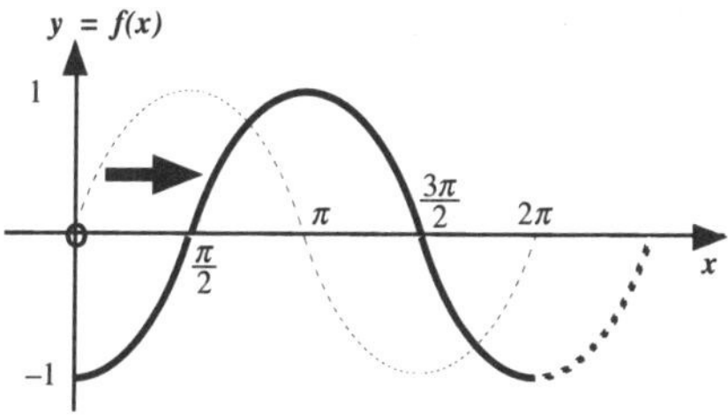

When you shift a graph, make sure you only draw it for the domain specified. Any extra parts of a cycle (shown heavy broken here) must not be included.

Example 2: Sketch the curve $y = \cos(2x + \frac{\pi}{2}) + 2$ for $0 \le x \le 2\pi$.

$b = 2$ 2 cycles, period $= \pi$

$c = 2$ vertical shift of centre line by 2

$2x + \frac{\pi}{2} = 0$

$2x = -\frac{\pi}{2}$

$= -\frac{\pi}{4}$

The graph will be a cosine curve starting at $-\frac{\pi}{4}$*,*

ie a shift of $\frac{\pi}{4}$ *to the left.*

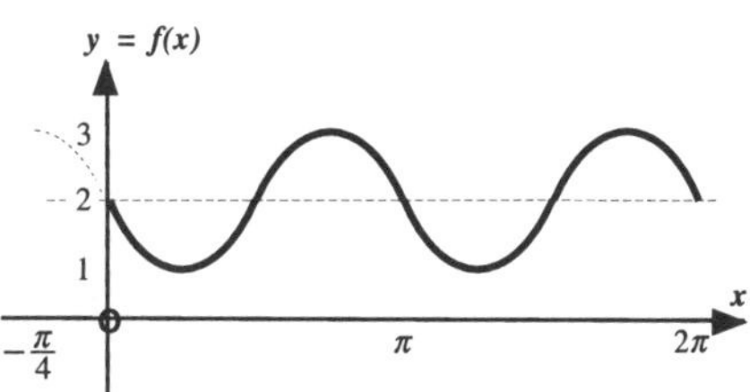

1.2.18 Maximum / Minimum Values of $f(x) = a\sin(bx + c) + d$ (or cos)

You can find the maximum or minimum value of a trig function, and where it occurs, without using calculus, by making use of graphical ideas.

In an exam question, you would not have more than two or three of a, b, c and d present at one time.

$\sin(bx + c)$ and $\cos(bx + c)$ have a maximum value of **1** and a minimum value of **−1**.

$a\sin(bx + c)$ and $a\cos(bx + c)$ have a maximum value of a and a minimum value of $-a$.

$a\sin(bx + c) + d$ and $a\cos(bx + c) + d$ have a maximum value of $a + d$ and a minimum value of $-a + d$.

For the sine functions, the maximum will occur when $bx^\circ + c = 90^\circ$ or $bx + c = \frac{\pi}{2}$, and the minimum will occur when $bx^\circ + c = 270^\circ$ or $bx + c = \frac{3\pi}{2}$.

For the cosine functions, the maximum will occur when $bx^\circ + c = 0^\circ$ or $bx + c = 0$, and the minimum will occur when $bx^\circ + c = 180^\circ$ or $bx + c = \pi$.

Example 1: State the maximum value of $f(x) = 3\sin(2x - \frac{\pi}{2})$ and find a value of x where it occurs.

sin has a max value of 1
3 sin (...) has a max value of $3 \times 1 = 3$
$f(x)$ has a maximum value of **3**.

$$2x - \frac{\pi}{2} = \frac{\pi}{2}$$
$$2x = \frac{\pi}{2} + \frac{\pi}{2} = \pi$$
$$x = \frac{\pi}{2}$$

Maxmum value occurs when $x = \frac{\pi}{2}$.

These methods can also be useful when drawing a graph of a function of the form $f(x) = a \sin(bx + c) + d$.

Example 2: Sketch the graph of $y = 5 \sin(30x - 60)^\circ$ for $0 \le x \le 12$.

period $= \dfrac{360}{30} = 12$ — 1 complete cycle of a sin curve

maximum $= 5$ — minimum $= -5$

zeros when	$30x - 60 = 0$	$30x - 60 = 180$	$30x - 60 = 360$
	$30x = 60$	$30x = 240$	$30x = 420$
	$x = 2$	$x = 8$	$x = 14$
			(out of domain)

Max when	$30x - 60 = 90$	Min when	$30x - 60 = 270$
	$30x = 150$		$30x = 330$
	$x = 5$		$x = 11$

$x = 0$ $\quad 5\sin(30x - 60)^\circ = -4.3$ to 1 dp

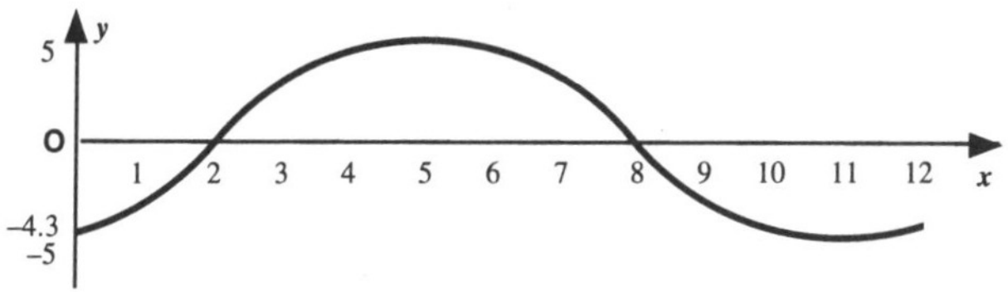

1.2.19 Exponential Functions

A function of the form

$f(x) = a^x, \quad a > 0$

is called an **exponential function**.

(See Section 3.3 for further details on exponential functions.)

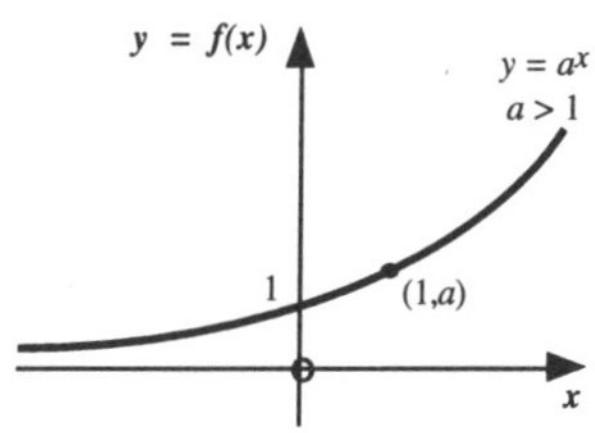

Since $a^0 = 1$ and $a^1 = a$, every exponential function will pass through $(0,1)$ and $(1,a)$.

The shape of the graph will depend on whether $a > 1$ or $0 < a < 1$, as shown.

When $a > 1$, the function will increase and this is called **exponential growth**.

When $0 < a < 1$, the function will decrease and this is called **exponential decay**.

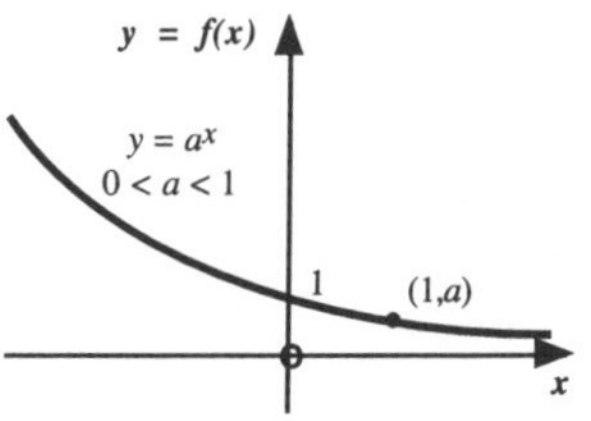

Example: On the same set of axes show the graphs of

(a) $y = 2^x$ and $y = 4^x$, (b) $y = 2^x$ and $y = \left(\frac{1}{2}\right)^x$.

(a)

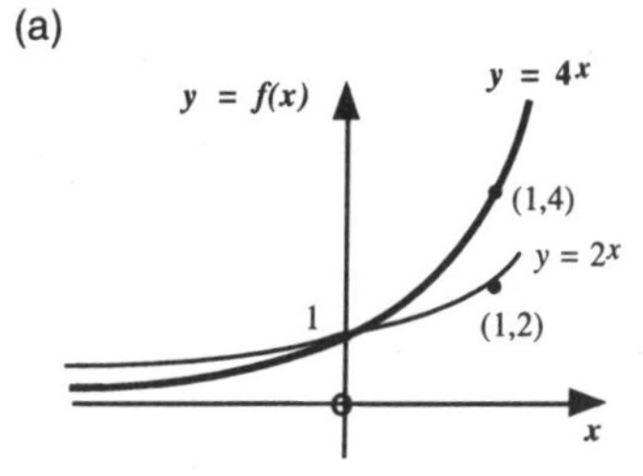

(b)

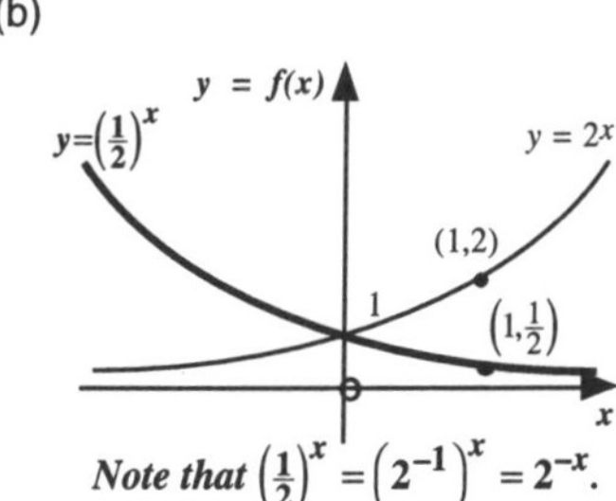

Note that $\left(\frac{1}{2}\right)^x = \left(2^{-1}\right)^x = 2^{-x}$.

1.2.20 Logarithmic Functions

Each exponential function has an inverse function of the form

$f(x) = \log_a x, \qquad a > 0$

It is called a **logarithmic function**.
It is only defined for $x > 0$.

(See Section 3.3 for further details on logarithmic functions.)

Since $\log_a 1 = 0$ and $\log_a a = 1$, every logarithmic function will pass through $(1,0)$ and $(a,1)$.

For Higher, you only need to know the shape of the graph when $a > 1$.

Example: On the same set of axes show the graphs of $y = \log_2 x$ and $y = \log_4 x$.

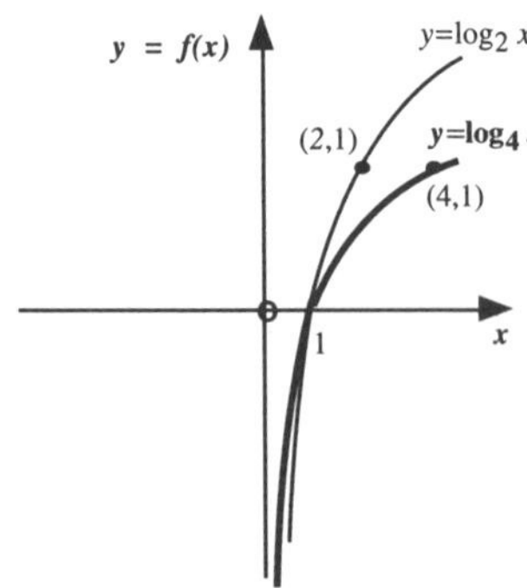

1.2.21 Graphs of Related Functions

Given the graph of a common function, you should be able to draw the graph of a related function (only simple polynomials and trig functions are explicitly mentioned in the syllabus). This graph can be sketched without knowing its formula.

The following changes to a function will produce a similar effect on the graph regardless of the type of function involved. You should be familiar with the general effect of each change. You can also consider the effect on a few key points on each graph to help determine the related graph.

You must find the images of any given points and annotate them on your sketch.

The Graph of $y = f(x) + k$

Adding or subtracting a constant k to a function has the effect of shifting the graph up or down vertically by k units.
Each point (x,y) will map onto the point $(x,y + k)$.

eg

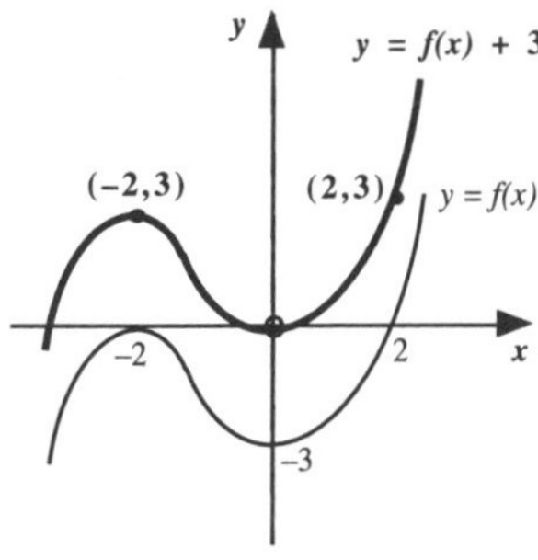

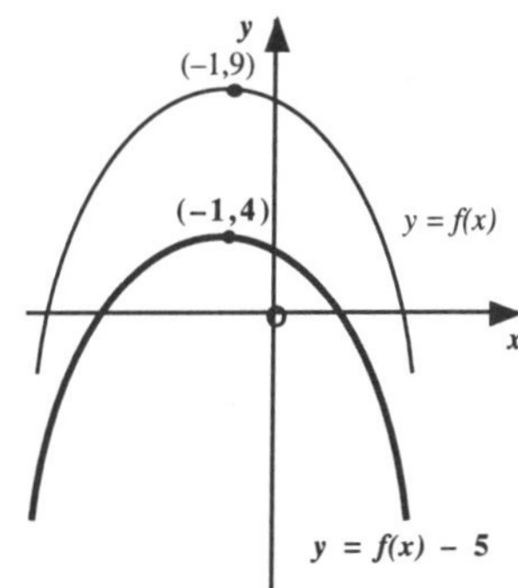

The Graph of $y = kf(x)$

Multiplying a function by a constant k has the effect of stretching or squeezing the graph vertically about the x-axis. If the constant is negative, this will also have the effect of reflecting the graph about the x-axis.
Each point (x,y) will map onto the point (x,ky).

eg

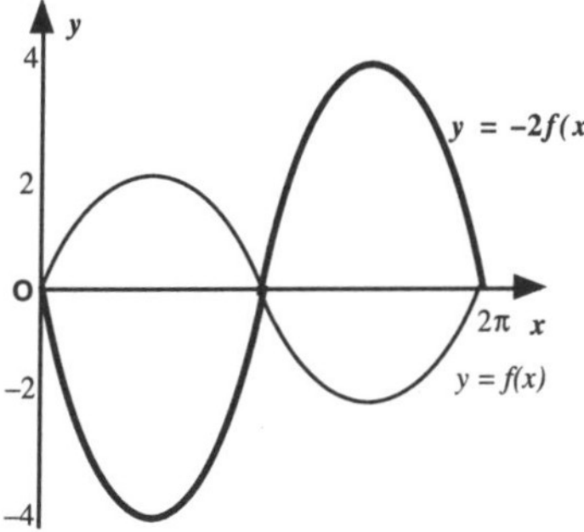

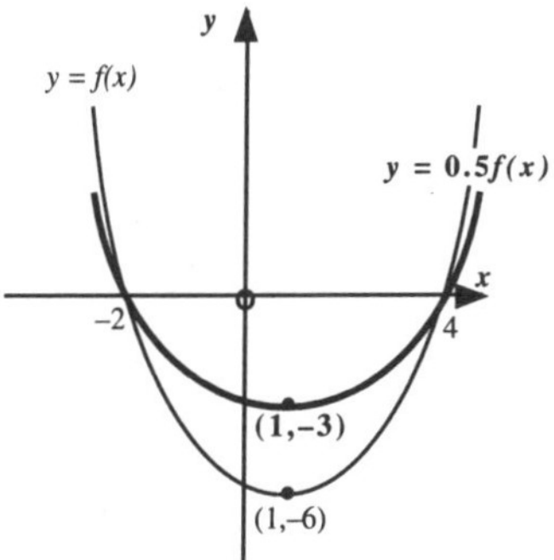

The Graph of $y = f(kx)$

Multiplying x by a constant k has the effect of stretching or squeezing the graph horizontally along the x-axis. The first example below shows the graph being squeezed in towards the y-axis ($k = 2$). The second example shows the graph being stretched ($k = 0.5$).

Each point (x, y) will map onto the point $\left(\frac{x}{k}, y\right)$.

eg

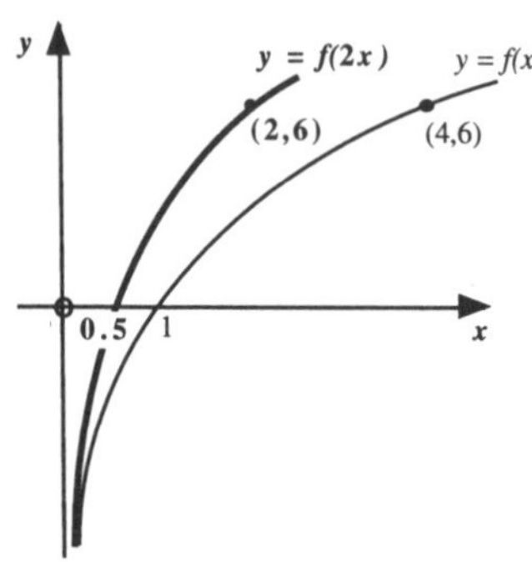

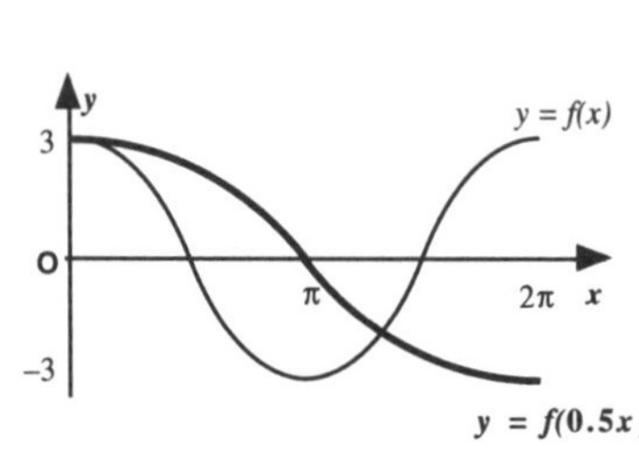

The Graph of $y = f(x + k)$

Adding or subtracting a constant k to the x term has the effect of shifting the graph left or right along the x-axis.
Each point (x, y) will map onto the point $(x - k, y)$.

eg

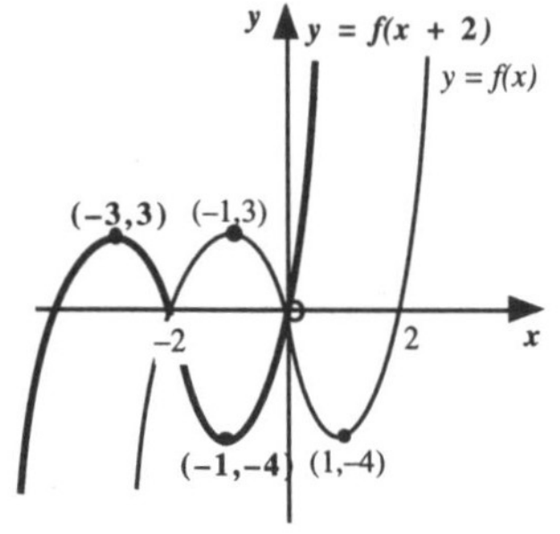

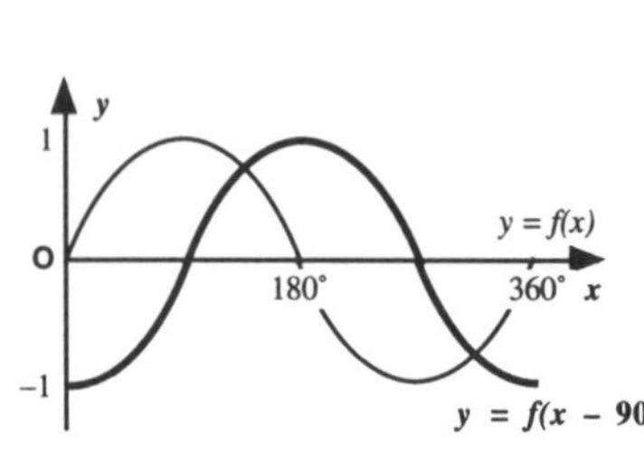

The Graph of $y = af(bx + c) + d$

You should be able to draw the resultant graph when a function is affected by a combination of two or more of the above effects. It often helps to work out the changes step by step.

Example: Draw the graph of $y = g(x)$ where the graph of the function $y = f(x)$ is shown, indicating the images of any points shown.

(a) $g(x) = 2f(x + 1)$ (b) $g(x) = 6 + f(2x)$ (c) $g(x) = 2f(x) - 15$

(a) ***Draw $f(x + 1)$ first - shown broken.***

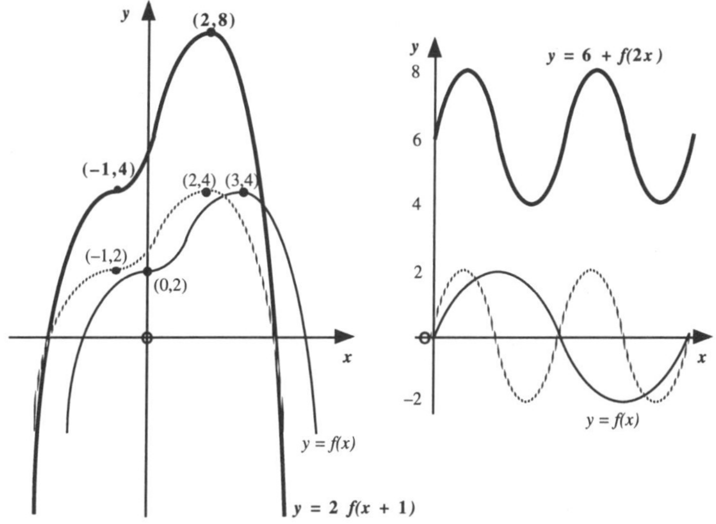

(c)

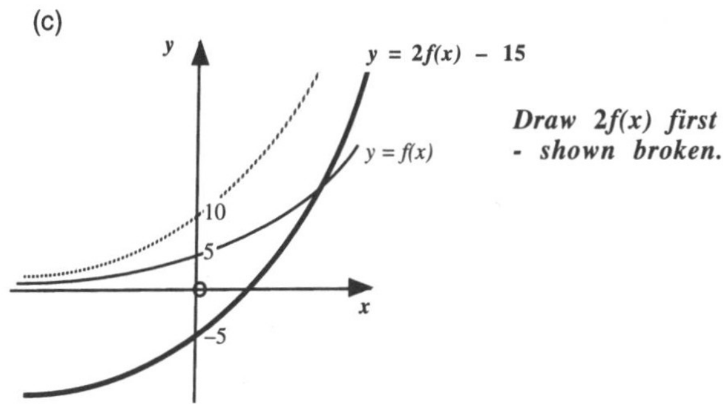

1.2.22 The Graph of the Derivative Function $f'(x)$

The derivative function $f'(x)$ is defined to be the function which gives the gradient value at any point on the curve $y = f(x)$. The derivative function is often called the gradient function because of this. (You are advised to wait until you have covered the theory in Section 1.3 before attempting this section).

To sketch the derivative function:

1. Identify any stationary points on $y = f(x)$. They will give the zeros of the gradient function.
2. Check where the function $y = f(x)$ is inceasing (decreasing). The derivative is positive (negative) on those intervals, and so the gradient function will be above (below) the x-axis on those intervals.

Example: Sketch the graph of $y = f'(x)$ where the graph of $y = f(x)$ is given.

> ***Unless you have additional information about the gradient of the graph of $y = f(x)$ at particular points, you will not be able to find the actual values of $f'(x)$. You will be able to give its general shape.***

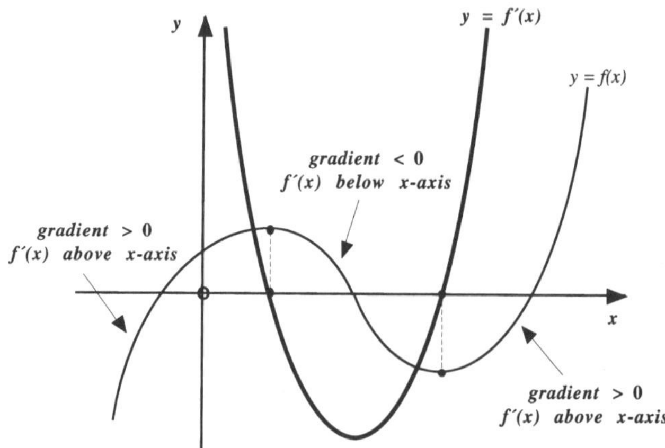

1.3 BASIC DIFFERENTIATION

1.3.1 The Meaning of a Derivative

The **derivative** of a function $f(x)$ is a measure of how the function changes as x changes. In general, this will give the **rate of change** of the function. In the context of a graph, it will be a measure of the **steepness** of the curve.

The gradient formula can only be used to find the gradient of a straight line. On a curve, the gradient is continually changing.

The **gradient at a point** on a curve is defined to be **the gradient of the tangent to the curve at that point.**

The **tangent to a curve** at a point is the straight line which just touches the curve at that point.

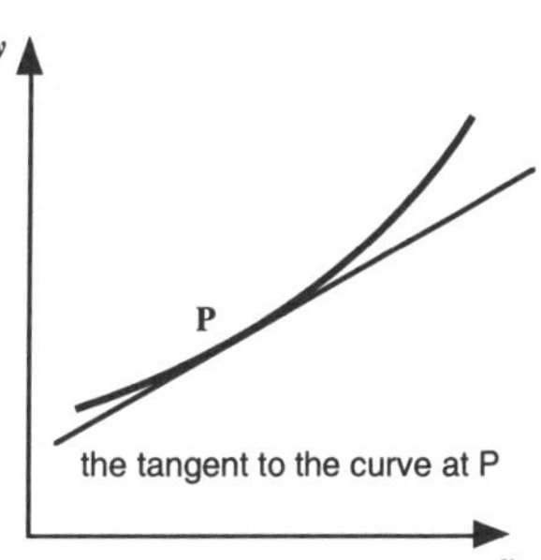

You can find the gradient of the chord joining two points on a curve using the gradient formula.

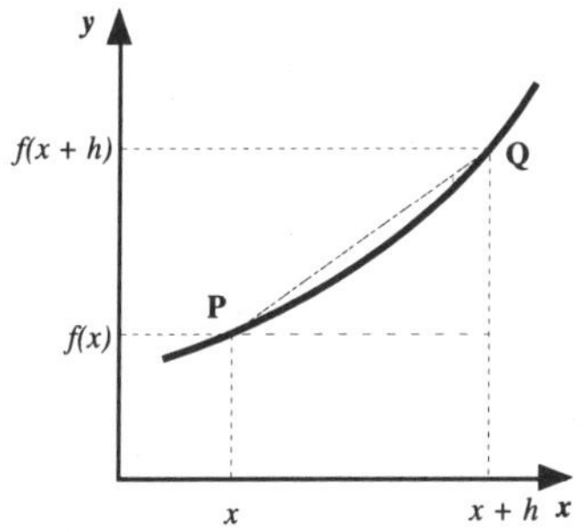

$$\text{gradient } PQ = \frac{y_2 - y_1}{x_2 - x_1} = \frac{f(x+h) - f(x)}{(x+h) - x} = \frac{f(x+h) - f(x)}{h}$$

If Q is then moved closer to P, ie as h gets smaller, the chord PQ will become nearer to the tangent at P. So the gradient of PQ will get closer to the value of the gradient of the tangent at P.

The gradient of the curve is defined to be $\lim\limits_{h \to 0} \dfrac{f(x+h) - f(x)}{h}$.

This is the formal definition of **the derivative of $f(x)$ with respect to x.**

You should know this but will <u>not</u> have to use it in the Higher exam.

1.3.2 Notation and Terminology

If f is a function of x, the derivative is called **the derivative of f with respect to x**. To find the derivative of a function, you **differentiate** it.

If a function can be differentiated at a point, you say it is **differentiable at that point**. If it can be differentiated over an interval of values, it is **differentiable over an interval**.

The derivative of a function will be a function itself and is called the **derived function** or, sometimes, the **gradient function**.

There is a variety of symbols used for the derivative:

when using	$y = \ldots$,	you usually use	$\frac{dy}{dx}$	(you say "dy by dx")
when using	$f(x) = \ldots$,	you usually use	$f'(x)$	(you say "f dash x")
when using an expression,		you usually use	$\frac{d}{dx}(\ldots)$	(you say "d by dx of ...")

1.3.3 The Rules for Differentiating

In practice, you do not use the formal definition to find a derivative. Instead, there are a few simple rules. The basic rule allows you to differentiate powers of x.

$$f(x) = x^n \quad \rightarrow \quad f'(x) = nx^{n-1}$$

Example 1:

$$f(x) = x^5$$
$$f'(x) = 5x^4$$

Example 2:

$$f(x) = x^{-3}$$
$$f'(x) = -3x^{-4}$$

Example 3:

$$f(x) = x^{\frac{1}{2}}$$
$$f'(x) = \tfrac{1}{2}x^{-\frac{1}{2}}$$

This can be extended to multiples and sums or differences of powers of x.

$$f(x) = ax^n \quad \rightarrow \quad f'(x) = anx^{n-1}$$

$$f(x) = ax^n + bx^m \quad \rightarrow \quad f'(x) = anx^{n-1} + bmx^{m-1}$$

Notice that the derivative of a constant will always be zero (see Example 5).

Example 4:

$$f(x) = 5x^4$$
$$f'(x) = 5 \times 4x^3$$
$$= \mathbf{20x^3}$$

Example 5:

$$f(x) = 2x^2 - 9x + 5$$
$$f'(x) = 2 \times 2x^1 - 9 \times 1x^0 + 0$$
$$= \mathbf{4x - 9}$$

Example 6:

$$f(x) = 2x^3 - 9x^{\frac{2}{3}}$$
$$f'(x) = 2 \times 3x^2 - 9 \times \tfrac{2}{3}x^{-\frac{1}{3}}$$
$$= \mathbf{6x^2 - 6x^{-\frac{1}{3}}}$$

Any brackets must first be multiplied out until you have a sum or difference of powers of x, and then differentiate.

Example 7:

$$f(x) = (x+3)(x-2)$$
$$= x^2 + x - 6$$
$$f'(x) = \mathbf{2x + 1}$$

Example 8:

$$f(x) = (2x+3)^2$$
$$= 4x^2 + 12x + 9$$
$$f'(x) = \mathbf{8x + 12}$$

1.3.4 Revision of Indices

The differentiation rules will only work with powers of x. In order to differentiate, you must be able to convert a function involving roots, fractions, brackets, etc, into a sum or difference of powers of x using the index definitions and rules from Standard Grade Maths. A good grasp on this is essential.

The Index Definitions

1.	$a^0 = 1$	2.	$a^{-n} = \dfrac{1}{a^n}$
3.	$a^{\frac{1}{n}} = \sqrt[n]{a}$	4.	$a^{\frac{m}{n}} = \sqrt[n]{(a^m)} = \left(\sqrt[n]{a}\right)^m$

The Index Rules

1.	$a^m \times a^n = a^{m+n}$	2.	$a^m \div a^n = a^{m-n}$
3.	$\left(a^m\right)^n = a^{mn}$	4.	$(ab)^n = a^n b^n$

Example 1:

$$\frac{1}{x^2} = \boldsymbol{x^{-2}}$$

Example 2:

$$\sqrt{x^3} = \boldsymbol{x^{\frac{3}{2}}}$$

Example 3:

$$\frac{2}{\sqrt[3]{x^2}} = \boldsymbol{2x^{-\frac{2}{3}}}$$

You may wish to change back to positive index form after differentiating.

Example 4:

$$3x^{-3} = \boldsymbol{\frac{3}{x^3}}$$

Example 5:

$$-\tfrac{1}{2}x^{-\frac{1}{2}} = \boldsymbol{\frac{-1}{2x^{\frac{1}{2}}}}$$

Example 6:

$$\tfrac{3}{2}x^{-\frac{2}{3}} = \boldsymbol{\frac{3}{2x^{\frac{2}{3}}}}$$

Example 7:

$$\begin{aligned}
&\sqrt{x}\left(2\sqrt{x} - \frac{2}{3\sqrt{x}}\right) \\
&= x^{\frac{1}{2}}\left(2x^{\frac{1}{2}} - \tfrac{2}{3}x^{-\frac{1}{2}}\right) \\
&= 2x^{\frac{1}{2}} \times x^{\frac{1}{2}} - \tfrac{2}{3} \times x^{\frac{1}{2}} \times x^{-\frac{1}{2}} \\
&= 2x^{\frac{1}{2}+\frac{1}{2}} - \tfrac{2}{3} \times x^{\frac{1}{2}-\frac{1}{2}} \\
&= 2x^1 - \tfrac{2}{3}x^0 \\
&= \boldsymbol{2x - \tfrac{2}{3}}
\end{aligned}$$

Example 8:

$$\begin{aligned}
&\frac{\left(4x^2 + 3x\right)}{2\sqrt{x}} \\
&= \tfrac{1}{2}x^{-\frac{1}{2}}\left(4x^2 + 3x\right) \\
&= \tfrac{1}{2} \times 4 \times x^{-\frac{1}{2}} \times x^2 + \tfrac{1}{2} \times 3 \times x^{-\frac{1}{2}} \times x \\
&= 2x^{-\frac{1}{2}+2} + \tfrac{3}{2} \times x^{-\frac{1}{2}+1} \\
&= \boldsymbol{2x^{\frac{3}{2}} + \tfrac{3}{2}x^{\frac{1}{2}}}
\end{aligned}$$

1.3.5 Using the Differentiation Rules - Harder Examples

1. First use the index definitions and rules to prepare the function for differentiating.
2. Use the differentiation rules to find the derivative.
3. If necessary, use the index definitions and rules to give the derivative using positive indices.

Note: For a differentiation question, there are normally no marks awarded for changing the form of the derivative once you have obtained it. However, if you have to go further and use it to evaluate the derivative at a point or solve an equation, it may be easier to have positive indices.

Example 1:

$$f(x) = 2x^5 - \frac{3}{x^2}$$
$$= 2x^5 - 3x^{-2}$$
$$f'(x) = 10x^4 + 6x^{-3}$$

This answer would be acceptable

$$= \mathbf{10x^4 + \frac{6}{x^3}}$$

Example 2:

$$f(x) = \sqrt{x}\left(2\sqrt{x} - \frac{3}{\sqrt{x}}\right)$$
$$= x^{\frac{1}{2}}\left(2x^{\frac{1}{2}} - 3x^{-\frac{1}{2}}\right)$$
$$= 2x^{\frac{1}{2}+\frac{1}{2}} - 3x^{\frac{1}{2}-\frac{1}{2}}$$
$$= 2x^1 - 3x^0$$
$$= 2x - 3$$
$$f'(x) = \mathbf{2}$$

Example 3:

$$f(x) = \frac{2x - x^3}{3\sqrt{x}}$$
$$= \tfrac{1}{3}x^{-\frac{1}{2}}\left(2x - x^3\right)$$
$$= \tfrac{1}{3}x^{-\frac{1}{2}} \times 2x - \tfrac{1}{3}x^{-\frac{1}{2}} \times x^3$$
$$= \tfrac{1}{3} \times 2 \times x^{-\frac{1}{2}+1} - \tfrac{1}{3}x^{-\frac{1}{2}+3}$$
$$= \tfrac{2}{3}x^{\frac{1}{2}} - \tfrac{1}{3}x^{\frac{5}{2}}$$

$$f'(x) = \tfrac{2}{3} \times \tfrac{1}{2}x^{-\frac{1}{2}} - \tfrac{1}{3} \times \tfrac{5}{2}x^{\frac{3}{2}}$$
$$= \tfrac{1}{3}x^{-\frac{1}{2}} - \tfrac{5}{6}x^{\frac{3}{2}}$$

This answer would be acceptable

$$= \mathbf{\frac{1}{3x^{\frac{1}{2}}} - \tfrac{5}{6}x^{\frac{3}{2}}}$$

When evaluating without having access to a calculator, it may be more helpful to use roots instead of fractional indices as shown below.

$$= \frac{1}{3\sqrt{x}} - \frac{5\sqrt{x^3}}{6}$$

1.3.6 Using the Derivative

There are two main contexts in which you differentiate a function -

1. mathematical (often involving graphing), and
2. real life,

although there can often be an overlap between the two.

In each of these, there are two main approaches to questions -

1. finding the value of the derivative at a particular point, and
2. finding where the derivative has the value zero.

This table summarises some of the common types of questions using each.

	Mathematical Context	Real Life Context
Evaluating $f'(x)$ at a particular value	Finding the gradient of a curve at a point. Finding where the curve has a particular gradient. Finding the equation of a tangent to a curve. Finding whether the curve is increasing or decreasing at a point.	Finding the rate of change of a quantity represented by a function, eg population, profit, height, volume. Finding the speed / acceleration at an instant given the distance / speed.
Finding where $f'(x) = 0$	Finding stationary points on a curve (often to sketch the curve) or the stationary values of a function. Finding the end points of the intervals on which a curve / function is increasing / decreasing. Finding the maximum / minimum values of a graph / function on an interval.	Finding the maximum / minimum of a quantity represented by a function, eg population, profit, height, volume. Finding the maximum / minimum speed / acceleration.

1.3.7 The Gradient / Equation of the Tangent to a Curve

The value of the derivative $f'(x)$ when $x = a$ is written $\boldsymbol{f'(a)}$.

$f'(a)$ will give the actual gradient of the curve $y = f(x)$, which is also the gradient of the tangent to the curve, at the point on the curve where $x = a$.

To find the equation of the tangent to a curve:

1. Use the derivative to find the gradient of the tangent at the point $x = a$.
2. Substitute $x = a$ into $y = f(x)$ to find the coordinates of the point on the curve.
3. Substitute these values into the straight line equation $y - b = m(x - a)$.

Example 1: Find the equation of the tangent to the curve $y = x^2 - 5x + 3$ when $x = 2$.

$$y = x^2 - 5x + 3$$
$$\frac{dy}{dx} = 2x - 5$$
$$x = 2 \qquad \frac{dy}{dx} = 2 \times 2 - 5 = -1$$
$$m = -1$$
$$x = 2 \qquad y = 2^2 - 5 \times 2 + 3 = -3$$

✔ $m = -1$ ✔ $(a,b) = (2,-3)$

$$y - b = m(x - a)$$
$$y - (-3) = -1(x - 2)$$
$$y + 3 = -x + 2$$
$$\mathbf{x + y = -1}$$

Example 2: Find the coordinates of the points where the gradient of the curve $y = x^3 - 2x^2 - 3x + 3$ makes an angle of 45° to the positive direction of the x-axis.

$\theta = 45^\circ \qquad m = \tan\theta = \tan 45^\circ = 1$ *Use the result $m = \tan\theta$ to find the gradient.*

$$y = x^3 - 2x^2 - 3x + 3$$
Differentiate y and equate the two.
$$\frac{dy}{dx} = 3x^2 - 4x - 3$$
$$\frac{dy}{dx} = 1$$
$$3x^2 - 4x - 3 = 1$$
$$3x^2 - 4x - 4 = 0$$
$$(3x + 2)(x - 2) = 0$$
$$3x + 2 = 0 \quad \text{or} \quad x - 2 = 0$$
$$3x = -2 \qquad x = 2$$
$$x = -\tfrac{2}{3}$$

$$y = x^3 - 2x^2 - 3x + 3$$
$$x = -\tfrac{2}{3} \qquad y = \left(-\tfrac{2}{3}\right)^3 - 2\left(-\tfrac{2}{3}\right)^2 - 3\left(-\tfrac{2}{3}\right) + 3$$
$$= -\tfrac{8}{27} - \tfrac{8}{9} + 2 + 3$$
$$y = 3\tfrac{22}{27} \qquad \text{(or 3.81 to 2 dp)}$$

$$x = 2 \qquad y = 2^3 - 2 \times 2^2 - 3 \times 2 + 3$$
$$= -3$$

The angle is 45° at $(-\tfrac{2}{3}, 3\tfrac{22}{27})$ and $(2,-3)$.

1.3.8 Stationary Points / Values

In the graph of $y = f(x)$, if $f'(a) = 0$, the curve has gradient 0 at $x = a$, and so is horizontal at that point. You say that the graph has a **stationary point** at $(a, f(a))$.

There are three types of stationary points.

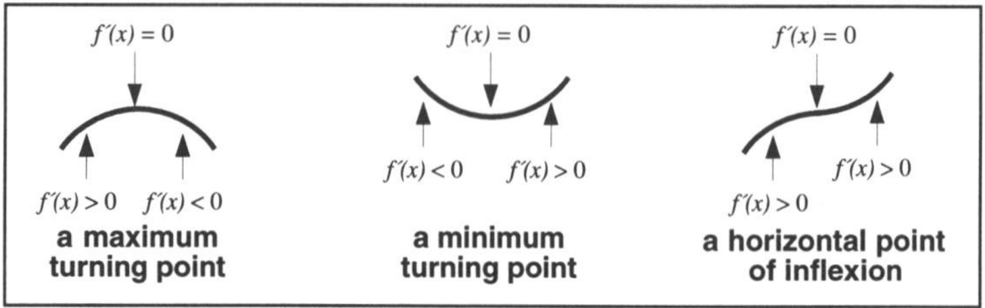

You can determine the **nature** of the stationary point by considering the value of $f'(x)$ on either side of a.

This is normally done using a **table of values**. The derivative is found for a value of x on either side of each solution to $f'(x) = 0$. The sign (positive or negative) of the derivative is what is important, not the actual value.

If you are considering a function rather than a graph, you normally talk about a **maximum** or **minimum stationary value** of the function. For a function $f(x)$, if $f'(a) = 0$, you say that the function f has a **stationary value of $f(a)$ at $x = a$.**

Whenever a stationary value or point is found, you must always check the nature.

Example 1: A curve has equation $y = x^4 + 8x^3 - 6$. Find algebraically the coordinates of the stationary points and determine their nature.

The word "algebraically" means you cannot read these off a graph. You must find the derivative, set it equal to zero, then solve the equation.

$$y = x^4 + 8x^3 - 6$$

$$\frac{dy}{dx} = 4x^3 + 24x^2$$

$$= 4x^2(x+6)$$

For stationary values, $\frac{dy}{dx} = 0$

$$4x^2(x+6) = 0$$

$$x^2 = 0 \quad \text{or} \quad x+6 = 0$$

$$x = 0 \qquad\qquad x = -6$$

Now check the value of $f'(x)$ at, for example, $x = -7, -6, -3, 0, 1$.

x	→	-6	→	0	→
$\frac{dy}{dx}$	$-$	0	$+$	0	$+$
y	\	—	/	—	/

$y = x^4 + 8x^3 - 6$

$x = -6 \qquad y = (-6)^4 + 8 \times (-6)^3 - 6 = -438$

Minimum turning point at **$(-6, -438)$.**

$x = 0 \qquad y = 0^4 + 8 \times 0^3 - 6 = -6$

Point of inflexion at **$(0, -6)$.**

Example 2: Find the stationary values of the function $f(x) = \frac{1}{3}x^3 + \frac{1}{2}x^2 - 6x$, and determine their nature.

$$f(x) = \tfrac{1}{3}x^3 + \tfrac{1}{2}x^2 - 6x$$
$$f'(x) = x^2 + x - 6$$
$$= (x - 2)(x + 3)$$

For stationary values, $f'(x) = 0$

$(x - 2)(x + 3) = 0$

$x - 2 = 0$ or $x + 3 = 0$

$x = 2 \qquad x = -3$

x	→	-3	→	2	→
$f'(x)$	$+$	0	$-$	0	$+$
$f(x)$	/	—	\	—	/

$$f(x) = \tfrac{1}{3}x^3 + \tfrac{1}{2}x^2 - 6x$$

$x = -3 \quad f(-3) = \frac{1}{3} \times (-3)^3 + \frac{1}{2} \times (-3)^2 - 6 \times (-3) = 13\frac{1}{2}$

f has a **maximum value** of **$13\frac{1}{2}$** at **$x = -3$.**

$x = 2 \quad f(2) = \frac{1}{3}(2)^3 + \frac{1}{2}(2)^2 - 6(2) = -7\frac{1}{3}$

f has a **minimum value** of **$-7\frac{1}{3}$** at **$x = 2$.**

Note: The above examples illustrate the most common method of determining the nature of the stationary points. You may prefer to look at each stationary point separately. There are various other methods also, eg factorising the derivative and using a table of factors or using the second derivative. If you have been taught one of these, then you should use it.

1.3.9 Strictly Increasing / Decreasing Functions

A function $f(x)$ is said to be
increasing at a point $x = a$ if $f'(a) > 0$,
and
decreasing at a point $x = a$ if $f'(a) < 0$.

To check whether a function is increasing or decreasing at a point, you must check the sign of $f'(x)$.

Example 1: The function $f(x) = 3x^2 - ax + 4$ is decreasing when $x = -2$. What are the possible values of a?

$$f(x) = 3x^2 - ax + 4$$
$$f'(x) = 6x - a$$

$f(x)$ is decreasing at $x = -2$, so $f'(-2) < 0$

$$6 \times (-2) - a < 0$$
$$-12 - a < 0$$
$$-a < 12$$
$$a > -12$$

$f(x)$ is decreasing at $x = -2$ when $\boldsymbol{a > -12}$.

A function $f(x)$ is said to be
strictly increasing on a given interval if $f'(x) > 0$ on that interval,
and
strictly decreasing on a given interval if $f'(x) < 0$ on that interval.

Note: Some textbooks use the term "increasing" for $f'(x) > 0$ on an interval and some use "increasing" for $f'(x) \geq 0$ on an interval. The definition given above is the one used in the Higher syllabus, so you should use it.

To check where a function is strictly increasing / decreasing, you can solve the inequation $f'(x) > 0$ / $f'(x) < 0$. However it is usually simpler to use a table of signs as you would to check for stationary points.

Example 2: $f(x)=\frac{1}{3}x^3-\frac{5}{2}x^2-6x+3$

On what interval is f (a) strictly increasing, (b) strictly decreasing?

$$f(x)=\tfrac{1}{3}x^3-\tfrac{5}{2}x^2-6x+3$$
$$f'(x)=\tfrac{1}{3}\times 3x^2-\tfrac{5}{2}\times 2x-6$$
$$=x^2-5x-6$$
$$=(x+1)(x-6)$$

For stationary values, $f'(x)=0$

$$(x+1)(x-6)=0$$
$$x+1=0 \quad \text{or} \quad x-6=0$$
$$x=-1 \qquad\qquad x=6$$

The stationary points will give the end points of the intervals.

x	→	−1	→	6	→
$f'(x)$	+	0	−	0	+
$f(x)$	/	—	\	—	/

(a) f is strictly increasing when $f'(x)>0$, ie $\mathbf{x<-1}$ **or** $\mathbf{x>6}$.

(b) f is strictly decreasing when $f'(x)<0$, ie $\mathbf{-1<x<6}$.

1.3.10 Curve Sketching

When **sketching** a curve you must find all the **significant** (or **critical) points** - where it cuts the axes and any stationary points. For a more accurate graph, it may be necessary to plot additional points.

It can be helpful to consider what the graph does as x becomes large ($x \rightarrow +\infty$) or small ($x \rightarrow -\infty$) to confirm your other findings.

To sketch a curve:

1. Find the **intersections with the axes**.

   You can find the intersection with the y-axis by substituting $x=0$ into the equation of the curve.
   You can find the intersection with the x-axis by setting $y=0$ and solving for x.

2. Find the **stationary points**.

   Use the methods from Section 1.3.8.

3. Check the **behaviour of the graph for large or small values of x.**

The term with the highest power of x will be **the most powerful term** in a function. A function will always act like its most powerful term as $x \rightarrow +\infty$ or as $x \rightarrow -\infty$.

If n is **even**	x^n **is positive as**	$x \rightarrow -\infty$
	and x^n **is positive as**	$x \rightarrow +\infty$.
If n is **odd**	x^n **is negative as**	$x \rightarrow -\infty$
	and x^n **is positive as**	$x \rightarrow +\infty$.

For example, $y = x^4 + 8x^3 - 6$ will act like x^4 for large and small values of x. So y is positive as $x \rightarrow -\infty$ and y is positive as $x \rightarrow +\infty$.

Remember to allow for a negative coefficient.

$y = x^2 - 2x^3$ will act like $-2x^3$ for large and small values of x.
So y is positive as $x \rightarrow -\infty$ and y is negative as $x \rightarrow +\infty$.
(The coefficient -2 reverses the effect produced by the odd power.)

4. **Annotate the graph** with all the significant points labelled.

Note: Complete curve sketching questions are no longer common in the Higher exam. The emphasis now is usually on finding intercepts and stationary points algebraically. This avoids disadvantaging pupils who do not have access to a graphic calculator. You should still know all the steps to produce a final sketch.

Example: Find the intercepts with the axes and the stationary points for the curve with equation $y = x^3 - 3x^2$, and sketch the curve.

Intercepts with axes:

y-axis: $x = 0$ $\quad y = x^3 - 3x^2 = 0^3 - 3 \times 0^2 = 0$ $\quad$ **(0,0)**

x-axis: $y = 0$ $\quad x^3 - 3x^2 = 0$

$$x^2(x-3) = 0$$

$$x^2 = 0 \quad \text{or} \quad x - 3 = 0$$

$$x = 0 \qquad\qquad x = 3$$

(0,0) **(3,0)**

Stationary Points:

$$y = x^3 - 3x^2$$

$$\frac{dy}{dx} = 3x^2 - 6x$$

For stationary points

$$\frac{dy}{dx} = 0$$

$$3x^2 - 6x = 0$$

$$3x(x-2) = 0$$

$x = 0$ or $x - 2 = 0$

$x = 2$

x	→	0	→	2	→
$\frac{dy}{dx}$	+	0	–	0	+
y	/	—	\	—	/

$x = 0$ $\quad y = (0)^3 - 3\times(0)^2$
$= 0$

Maximum turning point at $(0,0)$.

$x = 2$ $\quad y = (2)^3 - 3\times(2)^2$
$= -4$

Minimum turning point at $(2,-4)$.

Large / small values of x:

$x \to +\infty \quad y \to x^3$ - positive

$x \to -\infty \quad y \to x^3$ - negative

Annotate the graph:

All significant points must be clearly annotated. You can either give the coordinates, or show the appropriate values on the axes as with the minimum turning point.

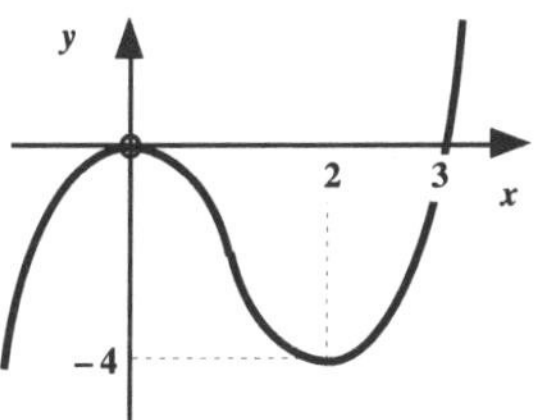

1.3.11 Rate of Change Problems

If f is a function of time t, the derivative of the function, $f'(t)$, gives the rate at which the function is changing with respect to time. This can be applied to a variety of contexts.

One important context for this is distance, speed and acceleration.
Speed (or velocity) is the **rate of change of distance** with time.
Acceleration is the **rate of change of speed** with time.

distance	s
speed	$v = \dfrac{ds}{dt}$
acceleration	$a = \dfrac{dv}{dt}$

Note: The term **initial**, eg initial height, signals $t = 0$.
You say **"after 5 seconds"** to mean exactly 5 seconds after the start.

Example: A rocket is fired from the roof of a building.
The height above the ground, h metres, of the rocket t seconds after it was fired, is given by $h = 45 + 40t - 5t^2$.
(a) What was its initial speed when it was launched?
(b) When did the rocket hit the ground?

(a)

$$h = 45 + 40t - 5t^2$$

$$\text{speed} = \frac{dh}{dt}$$

$$= 40 - 10t$$

For initial conditions, t = 0.

$$t = 0 \quad \frac{dh}{dt} = 40$$

Initial speed = **40 m/s**

(b)

At ground level, h = 0.
Put h = 0 and solve the equation.
You must then pick the appropriate solution.

$$45 + 40t - 5t^2 = 0$$

$$-5\left(t^2 - 8t - 9\right) = 0$$

$$-5(t - 9)(t + 1) = 0$$

$$t - 9 = 0 \quad \text{or} \quad t + 1 = 0$$

$$t = 9 \qquad t = -1$$

In the context, t cannot be negative.

The rocket hit the ground **after 9 seconds**.

1.3.12 Maximum / Minimum on a Closed Interval

A function f will take its maximum or minimum value on a closed interval where $f'(x) = 0$ or at the end points of the interval.

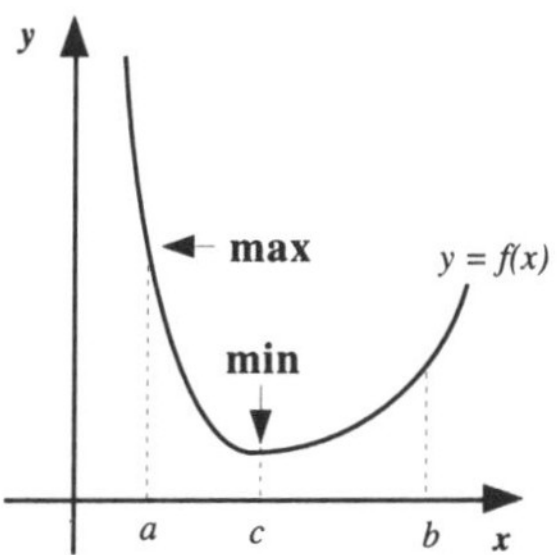

To find the maximum or minimum value, evaluate the function at each end point and at each stationary value within the interval.

For $a \leq x \leq b$, the function shown has a maximum value of $f(a)$ and a minimum value of $f(c)$.

Example: Find the maximum and minimum values of $f(x) = x^2 - 4x + 5$ on the interval $-2 \leq x \leq 5$.

$f(x) = x^2 - 4x + 5$

$f'(x) = 2x - 4$

For stationary values, $f'(x) = 0$.

$2x - 4 = 0$

$2x = 4$

$x = 2$

$f(x) = x^2 - 4x + 5$

Check end points and stationary values.

$f(-2) = (-2)^2 - 4 \times (-2) + 5 = 17$

$f(5) = 5^2 - 4 \times 5 + 5 = 10$

$f(2) = 2^2 - 4 \times 2 + 5 = 1$

Maximum value is **17**. Minimum value is **1**.

1.3.13 Maximum / Minimum (or Optimisation) Problems

When a real life problem is modelled with a function, the function will often only be valid for a particular domain. It is important to be aware of the appropriate domain in the context, and to state it.

A function f will take its maximum or minimum value when $f'(x) = 0$ or at the end points of a closed interval. You can use these ideas to find the maximum or minimum value of a function in context.

This process of finding the "best" value is often called **optimisation**.

Often in this type of problem, the function to be maximised or minimised contains two variables. You cannot differentiate a function with more than one variable. There will be an additional piece of information in the question which allows you to give the function in terms of one variable.

1. Identify the function to be maximised or minimised. Look for clues in the wording, eg biggest, smallest, fastest, cheapest, quickest, least, etc.
2. If there are two variables in this function, use an additional piece of information to give one variable in terms of the other. Substitute this into the main function.
3. Differentiate this function and find where the derivative is equal to zero. Check the nature of any stationary value.
4. Check on what interval the function is defined and whether the stationary value(s) are inside the interval.
5. Answer the question <u>in context</u> (not just $x = ...$).

Note: In the context of distance, speed and time:

at a maximum / minimum distance,	$\frac{ds}{dt} = 0$
at a maximum / minimum speed,	$\frac{dv}{dt} = 0$

Example 1: A rocket is fired from the roof of a building.
The height above the ground, h metres, of the rocket t seconds after it was fired, is given by $h = 45 + 40t - 5t^2$.
At what time did the rocket reach its maximum height, and what was this height?

$$h = 45 + 40t - 5t^2$$

Since h is a quadratic with a negative squared term, it will have a maximum stationary value.

$$\frac{dh}{dt} = 40 - 10t$$

At max height, $\frac{dh}{dt} = 0$

$$40 - 10t = 0$$
$$10t = 40$$
$$t = 4$$

$t = 4$ $\quad h = 45 + 40 \times 4 - 5 \times 4^2$
$= 125$

The maximum height is **125 metres**, and it is reached after **4 seconds**.

Example 2: A cylindrical container has to have a volume of 432π cm^3.
It is made of metal weighing 1.5 g/cm^2.
What should the dimensions of the container be to minimise its weight, and what will this minimum weight be?

Weight is based on the surface area of the cylinder.
The surface area formula must be minimised.

In the exam, questions like this often start with a "Show that A = ..." part. This allows you to make use of the formula even if you cannot show it yourself.

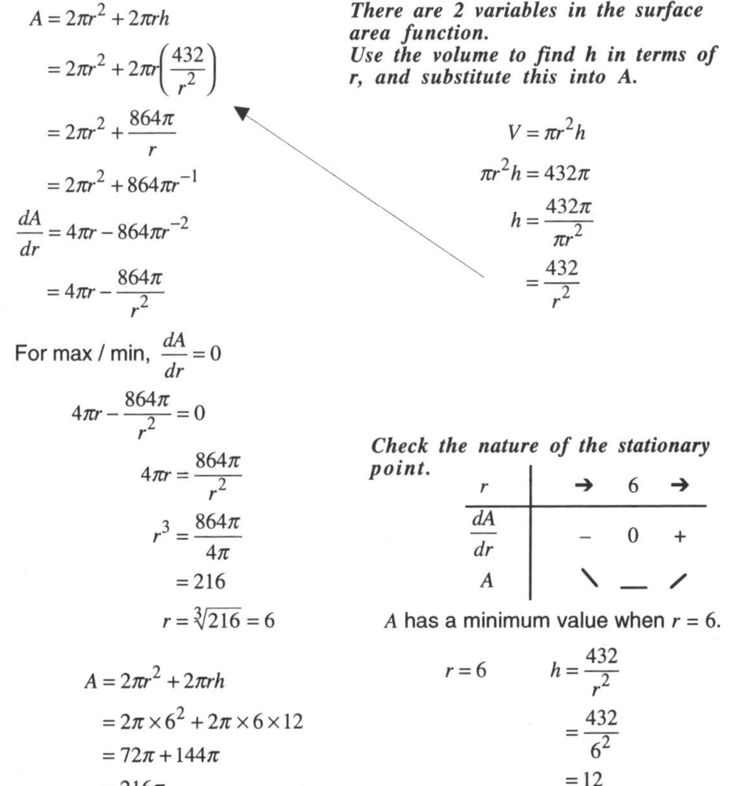

$$
\begin{aligned}
A &= 2\pi r^2 + 2\pi rh \\
&= 2\pi r^2 + 2\pi r\left(\frac{432}{r^2}\right) \\
&= 2\pi r^2 + \frac{864\pi}{r} \\
&= 2\pi r^2 + 864\pi r^{-1} \\
\frac{dA}{dr} &= 4\pi r - 864\pi r^{-2} \\
&= 4\pi r - \frac{864\pi}{r^2}
\end{aligned}
$$

There are 2 variables in the surface area function.
Use the volume to find h in terms of r, and substitute this into A.

$$
\begin{aligned}
V &= \pi r^2 h \\
\pi r^2 h &= 432\pi \\
h &= \frac{432\pi}{\pi r^2} \\
&= \frac{432}{r^2}
\end{aligned}
$$

For max / min, $\frac{dA}{dr} = 0$

$$
\begin{aligned}
4\pi r - \frac{864\pi}{r^2} &= 0 \\
4\pi r &= \frac{864\pi}{r^2} \\
r^3 &= \frac{864\pi}{4\pi} \\
&= 216 \\
r &= \sqrt[3]{216} = 6
\end{aligned}
$$

Check the nature of the stationary point.

r	→	6	→
$\frac{dA}{dr}$	–	0	+
A	↘	—	↗

A has a minimum value when $r = 6$.

$$
\begin{aligned}
A &= 2\pi r^2 + 2\pi rh \\
&= 2\pi \times 6^2 + 2\pi \times 6 \times 12 \\
&= 72\pi + 144\pi \\
&= 216\pi
\end{aligned}
$$

$$
r = 6 \qquad h = \frac{432}{r^2} = \frac{432}{6^2} = 12
$$

$$
\begin{aligned}
\text{Weight} &= 216\pi \times 1.5 \\
&= 324\pi \quad (\approx 1018)
\end{aligned}
$$

The cylinder should have **radius 6 cm** and **height 12 cm** to have minimum weight. The minimum weight will be **324π grams** (approximately 1018 grams).

1.4 RECURRENCE RELATIONS

1.4.1 Sequences

A **sequence** is a list of numbers whose order follows some mathematical pattern. It is useful to identify each term in a sequence using the notation u_n, where u_n represents the nth **term** in the sequence,

eg	u_1	u_2	u_3	u_4	u_5	...	u_n
	↓	↓	↓	↓	↓	...	↓
	4	7	10	13	16	...	?

If you can obtain a formula for u_n, you call this the **formula for the nth term**. It then allows you to find any term directly. In the above example, $u_n = 3n + 1$.

It is not always possible to find a formula for the nth term. Instead, you may be able to obtain a formula to find the **next term**, u_{n+1}, given any term in a sequence.

In the above example, you add 3 each time. You can write this as $u_{n+1} = u_n + 3$, where u_n is any term in the sequence and u_{n+1} is the next term.

A formula of this form is called a **recurrence relation**.

1.4.2 Linear Recurrence Relations

In the Higher course, you will only meet **linear recurrence relations** which have the form

$$\boxed{u_{n+1} = au_n + b}$$

where a and b are constants.

A sequence is fully defined by giving the recurrence relation and the **first term**. It is quite common to use u_0 for the first term, although sometimes u_1 is a better choice.

When using recurrence relations in practical contexts, you often want u_n to be the sequence value obtained after n applications of the rule.

Example: A sequence is defined by $u_{n+1} = 2u_n + 3$ where $u_0 = 5$.
Write the first 5 terms of the sequence.

$$u_{n+1} = 2u_n + 3$$
$$u_0 = \mathbf{5}$$
$$u_1 = 2u_0 + 3 = 2 \times 5 + 3 = \mathbf{13}$$
$$u_2 = 2u_1 + 3 = 2 \times 13 + 3 = \mathbf{29}$$
$$u_3 = 2u_2 + 3 = 2 \times 29 + 3 = \mathbf{61}$$
$$u_4 = 2u_3 + 3 = 2 \times 61 + 3 = \mathbf{125}$$

1.4.3 Behaviour of u_n as n Tends to Infinity

If the recurrence relation is repeatedly applied, the value of u_n can keep increasing (towards $+\infty$) or keep decreasing (towards $-\infty$) or get closer and closer to a particular value L.

In this case you say that **u_n tends to a limit, L, as n tends to infinity**. You write this **$u_n \rightarrow L$ as $n \rightarrow \infty$**.

For the recurrence relation $u_{n+1} = au_n + b$:

$u_n \rightarrow L$ *as* $n \rightarrow \infty$	**if and only if**	$-1 < a < 1$

When a limit exists, you can find it by using the following method.

$$u_{n+1} = au_n + b$$
$$\downarrow \quad \downarrow$$

As $n \rightarrow \infty$

$$L = aL + b$$
$$L - aL = b$$
$$L(1 - a) = b$$

As $n \rightarrow \infty$ both u_{n+1} and u_n will tend to L, so L must satisfy the equation L = aL + b.

$$\boxed{L = \frac{b}{1-a}}$$

To find a limit in a particular example, follow the same procedures using the figures in the question, as shown below, or use the formula.

Example: A sequence is defined by the recurrence relation $u_{n+1} = 0.7u_n - 5$ with first term u_0. Find the exact value of the limit of u_n as n tends to infinity.

This sequence will tend to a limit L since $-1 < 0.7 < 1$.

$$u_{n+1} = 0.7u_n - 5$$
$$\downarrow \quad \downarrow$$
As $n \to \infty$
$$L = 0.7L - 5$$
$$L - 0.7L = -5$$
$$0.3L = -5$$
$$L = \frac{-5}{0.3}$$
$$= -\tfrac{50}{3}$$

Any time you find or use a limit for a recurrence relation, you must explain why it exists by stating or showing that −1 < a < 1.

Multiply top and bottom by 10 to get rid of the decimal fraction. You can leave it as an improper fraction.

1.4.4 Applying Recurrence Relations in Contexts

Most examples in this topic are set in some practical or real life context. Each situation will involve a quantity which changes repeatedly in a regular manner.

There can be two effects causing this change - a constant value acting as a multiplier (often a percentage), and/or a constant amount being added or subtracted.

You require to model the situation with a recurrence relation. You normally set up the recurrence relation so that the multiplier acts first.

Each repetition of the changes is a **cycle** and the time taken for each cycle is called the **period** of the recurrence relation.

1. If necessary, try the question numerically until you are sure what is being asked.
2. A diagram identifying the different effects may help you decide what is involved in the relation and what the period of the cycle is.
3. Translate this into an algebraic relation, stating what the symbols represent.
4. Use the recurrence relation to answer the question.

Example 1: When a certain drug is administered to a patient, 40% of it will disappear from the body after 1 hour.
If a dose of 100 mg is administered each hour, how much will be present in the body immediately after the 4th dose?

Initial amount = 100 mg

Loss per hour = 40%. Left after each hour = 60%

Amount left after first hour = 60% of 100 mg

$= 0.6 \times 100 = 60$ mg

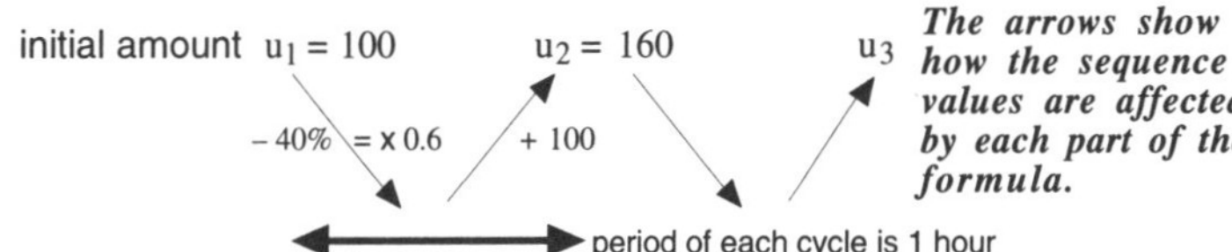

The arrows show how the sequence values are affected by each part of the formula.

The recurrence relation is $u_{n+1} = 0.6u_n + 100$,

where u_n is the amount of drug in the body after n doses.

In this case, use u_1 to represent the initial value.

$$u_1 = 100$$
$$u_2 = 0.6u_1 + 100 = 0.6 \times 100 + 100 = 160$$
$$u_3 = 0.6u_2 + 100 = 0.6 \times 160 + 100 = 196$$
$$u_4 = 0.6u_3 + 100 = 0.6 \times 196 + 100 = 217.6$$

There are **218 mg** of drug in the body after the 4th dose.

There may be more than one application of the multiplier (as in Example 2) or the add-on term (as in Example 3) in each cycle of the recurrence relation.

Example 2: The same drug as in Example 1 above is administered to a patient. If a dose of 100 mg is administered every 2 hours, how much will be present in the body immediately after the 4th dose?

Initial amount = 100 mg

Amount left after two hours = 60% of 60% of 100 mg

$= 0.6 \times 0.6 \times 100$

$= 0.6^2 \times 100$ mg

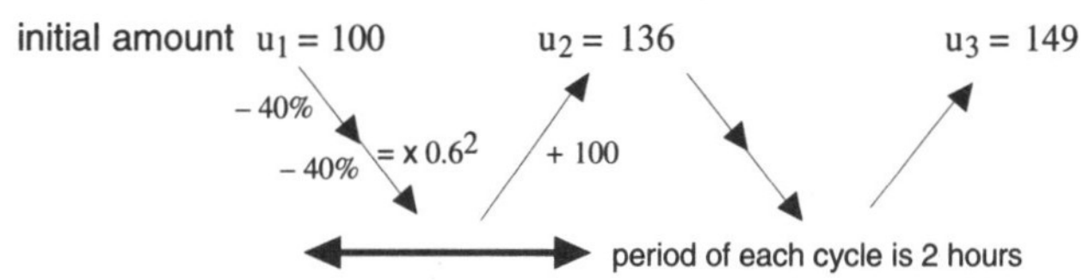

The recurrence relation is $u_{n+1} = 0.6^2 u_n + 100$,
where u_n is the amount of drug in the body after n doses.

Use u_1 to represent the initial value.

$$u_1 = 100$$
$$u_2 = 0.6^2 u_1 + 100 = 0.6^2 \times 100 + 100 = 136$$
$$u_3 = 0.6^2 u_2 + 100 = 0.6^2 \times 136 + 100 = 148.96$$
$$u_4 = 0.6^2 u_3 + 100 = u_2 \times 148.96 + 100 = 153.6...$$

There are **154 mg** of drug in the body after the 4th dose.

Example 3: A man borrows £1000 from a bank. Interest is charged at 5% on the amount outstanding at the start of each year. He pays £25 per month. In which year will he pay off the loan?

Initial amount	$= £1000$
Loan plus interest	$= £1000 + 5\%$ of $£1000$
	$= 1.05 \times 1000$
Payments each year	$= 12 \times £25 = £300$
Amount owing	$= 1.05 \times £1000 - £300$

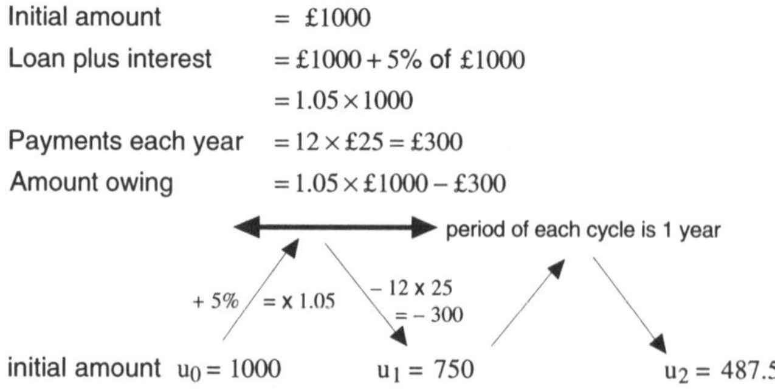

The recurrence relation is $u_{n+1} = 1.05u_n - 300$,
where u_n is the amount owing at the end of n years.

Use u_0 to represent the initial value.

$$u_0 = 1000$$
$$u_1 = 1.05u_0 - 300 = 1.05 \times 1000 - 300 = 750$$
$$u_2 = 1.05u_1 - 300 = 1.05 \times 750 - 300 = 487.5$$
$$u_3 = 1.05u_2 - 300 = 1.05 \times 487.5 - 300 = 211.87...$$
$$u_4 = 1.05u_3 - 300 = 1.05 \times 211.87... - 300 = -77.53...$$

The loan is paid off **during the 4th year.**

1.4.5 Applying Recurrence Relations in "Long Term" Contexts

Many examples in context involve considering what will happen if the situation is allowed to continue indefinitely. This is usually signalled by words like "in the long term".

In these cases you apply the techniques of section 1.4.3. You will often have to check out the situation against some stated conditions.

Example 1: There are estimated to be 800 fish in a pond. 35% of the fish are removed by anglers each year. The manager wants to maintain a stock of at least 600 fish. He decides to add 200 fish at the end of each year. Will this be a suitable policy in the long term?

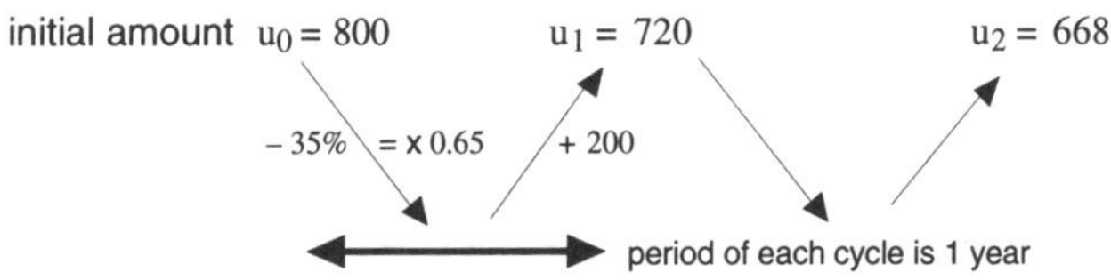

The recurrence relation is $u_{n+1} = 0.65u_n + 200$,
where u_n is the number of fish after n years.

Use u_0 to represent the initial value.

$$u_0 = 800$$
$$u_1 = 0.65u_0 + 200 = 0.65 \times 800 + 200 = 720$$
$$u_2 = 0.65u_1 + 200 = 0.65 \times 720 + 200 = 668$$
$$\downarrow$$
$u_n \to 571.42...$ as $n \to \infty$ (by repeated applications)

This sequence will tend to a limit L since $-1 < 0.65 < 1$.

$$u_{n+1} = 0.65u_n + 200$$
$$\downarrow \quad \downarrow$$

As $n \to \infty$

$$L = 0.65L + 200$$
$$L - 0.65L = 200$$
$$0.35L = 200$$
$$L = \frac{200}{0.35}$$
$$= 571.42...$$

You <u>must</u> obtain the limit algebraically, and explain why it exists by stating or showing that −1 < a < 1.

The policy will **not** be suitable in the long term as the fish population will tend to 571 **which is below the required target of 600.**

It may be necessary to check suitability in relation to both a maximum and minimum level. You must be clear whether the recurrence relation is giving maximum or minimum values (see Example 2 below). The diagram should help you decide this.

Example 2: A car takes a maximum of 4 litres of engine oil. The minimum safe level is 3 litres. The engine is losing 2.5% of its oil per day. The owner decides to add 0.5 litres at the end of each week. Will this be a suitable strategy to avoid the oil level falling below the minimum or going above the maximum levels?

Loss of oil = 2.5% per day for 7 days
Amount remaining after 1 week $= 0.975^7$

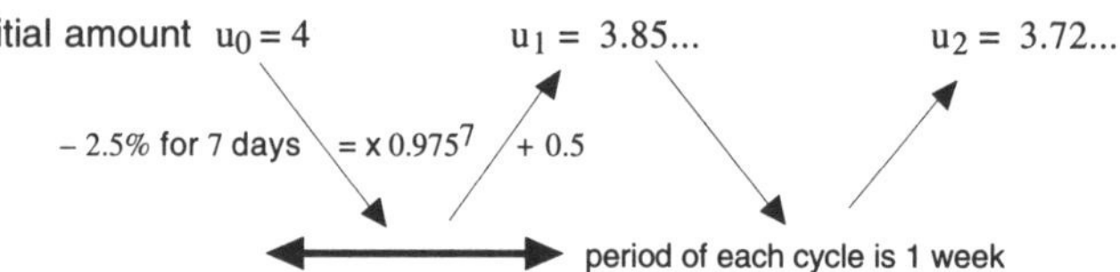

The recurrence relation is $u_{n+1} = 0.975^7 u_n + 0.5$,
where u_n is the number of litres after n weeks.

Use u_0 to represent the initial value.

$$u_0 = 4$$
$$u_1 = 0.975^7 u_0 + 0.5 = 0.975^7 \times 4 + 0.5 = 3.85...$$
$$u_2 = 0.975^7 u_1 + 0.5 = 0.975^7 \times 3.85... + 0.5 = 3.72...$$
$$\downarrow$$
$u_n \to 3.07...$ as $n \to \infty$ (by repeated applications)

This sequence will tend to a limit L since $-1 < 0.975^7 < 1$.

$$u_{n+1} = 0.975^7 u_n + 0.5$$
$$\downarrow \qquad \downarrow$$
As $n \to \infty$ $\quad L = 0.975^7 L + 0.5$

$$L - 0.975^7 L = 0.5$$
$$0.16... \times L = 0.5$$
$$L = \frac{0.5}{0.16...}$$
$$= 3.07...$$

In the long term, the oil level will tend to 3.1 litres using this strategy.

This is the value immediately after adding the oil, so **it will not go above the maximum limit of 4 litres**.

However, immediately before adding the 0.5 litres of oil, the level would be 2.6 litres, which is **below the minimum level of 3 litres**.

This would **not** be a satisfactory strategy therefore.

1.4.6 The Use of a Graphic Calculator

Graphic calculators, and some of the newer scientific calculators, have a "**Last Answer Memory**" button (often called **ANS**) which is extremely useful for recurrence relations.

It allows you to use the previous answer in the next calculation and repeat the same calculation with it. Each repetition of the recurrence relation then needs only one press of the button.

To evaluate $u_{n+1} = 0.7u_n - 5$ with first term $u_0 = 5$ on the calculator:

enter the initial term,
5 — press ENTER / EXECUTE

enter the recurrence relation using the ANS key for u_n,
0.7ANS – 5 — press ENTER / EXECUTE

continue to find the next term as often as required.
press ENTER / EXECUTE
press ENTER / EXECUTE
press ENTER / EXECUTE

This is very useful for finding specific terms when using a recurrence relation.

2.1 POLYNOMIALS AND QUADRATIC THEORY

2.1.1 Polynomials

An expression made up from a sum or difference of positive integer powers of x is called a **polynomial**. In general, if $f(x)$ is a polynomial, then:

$$f(x) = a_n x^n + a_{n-1}x^{n-1} + a_{n-2}x^{n-2} + \quad \dots \quad + a_2 x^2 + a_1 x + a_0$$

where $a_n, a_{n-1}, a_{n-2}, \dots, a_2, a_1, a_0$ are all real numbers, and n is a positive integer.

The highest power of x present in the polynomial is called the **degree** of the polynomial. $f(x)$ above has degree n.
The number a_n is called the **coefficient of x^n**.

2.1.2 Evaluating a Polynomial

A polynomial can be evaluated for a particular x value h by substituting h in place of x. This can be done repeatedly very quickly on a graphic calculator if you have one.

Example 1: Evaluate the polynomial $f(x) = 3x^4 - 4x^2 + 5x - 7$ for $x = -2$.

$$f(-2) = 3(-2)^4 - 4(-2)^2 + 5(-2) - 7 = \mathbf{15}$$

A polynomial can also be evaluated using the "synthetic" or "nested" method. The coefficients are arranged along the top row of a table. You must enter a zero for any power of x not present. To evaluate the polynomial for $x = h$, you add the numbers in the first two rows and enter the sum below the line, then multiply by h to obtain the next number in the second row, starting from the left and working to the right.

Example 2: Evaluate the polynomial $f(x) = 3x^4 - 4x^2 + 5x - 7$ for $x = -2$.

Coefficients of f(x)

−2	3	0	−4	5	−7
		−6	12	−16	22
	3	−6	8	−11	**15**

Evaluated at x = −2. **$f(-2) = 15$.**

Add
−4 + 12 = 8

0	−4	5
−6	12	−16
−6	8	−11

Multiply
8 x −2 = −16

2.1.3 Division of a Polynomial

The synthetic method can also be used to divide a polynomial $f(x)$ by $x - h$. When set up as above for evaluating a polynomial, the numbers in the third row give the **quotient** (answer) and the **remainder** when $f(x)$ is divided by $x - h$.

This method is known as **synthetic division**.

Example 1: Find the quotient and the remainder when the polynomial $f(x) = 2x^3 + 5x^2 - 10x + 4$ is divided by $x - 3$.

3	2	5	−10	4
		6	33	69
	2	11	23	73

↑ *Coefficients of quotient* — *Remainder* ↖

$(2x^3 + 5x^2 - 10x + 4) \div (x - 3)$

$= (2x^2 + 11x + 23) + 73$

Quotient $= \mathbf{2x^2 + 11x + 23}$

Remainder $= \mathbf{73}$.

When dividing by $x + h$, you must set up the synthetic method to evaluate for $-h$.

Example 2: Find the quotient and the remainder when the polynomial $f(x) = 3x^4 - 4x^2 + 5x - 7$ is divided by $x + 2$.

−2	3	0	−4	5	−7
		−6	12	−16	22
	3	−6	8	−11	15

$(3x^4 - 4x^2 + 5x - 7) \div (x + 2)$

$= (3x^3 - 6x^2 + 8x - 11) + 15$

Quotient $= \mathbf{3x^3 - 6x^2 + 8x - 11}$

Remainder $= \mathbf{15}$

2.1.4 The Remainder Theorem

From the above, you can see that the remainder of $f(x)$ on division by $x - h$ will always be $f(h)$. This is known as the **Remainder Theorem**.

> **When a polynomial $f(x)$ is divided by $x - h$, the remainder will be given by $f(h)$.**

Example: When $f(x) = x^3 - 2x^2 + ax + 2$ is divided by $x - 3$, the remainder is 5. Find the value of a.

$$\begin{array}{c|cccc} 3 & 1 & -2 & a & 2 \\ & & 3 & 3 & 3a+9 \\ \hline & 1 & 1 & a+3 & 3a+11 \end{array}$$

Remainder $= 5$

$$3a + 11 = 5$$
$$3a = -6$$
$$a = -2$$

2.1.5 The Factor Theorem

If the remainder on dividing $f(x)$ by $x - h$ is zero, then $x - h$ must be a factor of $f(x)$, and conversely, if $x - h$ is a factor, $f(h) = 0$. This is known as the **Factor Theorem**.

> **$x - h$ is a factor of $f(x)$ if and only if $f(h) = 0$.**

The Factor Theorem is used to factorise polynomials. You first find h values which give $f(h) = 0$. These will then give the factors of $f(x)$.

When asked to factorise $f(x)$ **completely**, you must find all the factors. Use the Factor Theorem to get started, then factorise quadratics as in Standard Grade.

It is useful to note that h values will often be factors of the constant term in $f(x)$.

Example 1: Factorise completely $f(x) = 2x^3 + 3x^2 - 32x + 15$.

Use trial and error with the factors of 15 (± 1, ± 3, ± 5) until you find a factor.
You can use either the synthetic method or a graphic calculator to do this quickly. Once you have found one factor, use the synthetic method to find the quotient so you can factorise it.

$$\begin{array}{c|cccc} 3 & 2 & 3 & -32 & 15 \\ & & 6 & 27 & -15 \\ \hline & 2 & 9 & -5 & 0 \end{array}$$

$$2x^3 + 3x^2 - 32x + 15$$
$$= (x - 3)(2x^2 + 9x - 5)$$
$$= \mathbf{(x - 3)(x + 5)(2x - 1)}$$

If the degree of $f(x)$ is greater than 3, you will usually have to find more than one factor. You can use the synthetic method repeatedly. Remember that some quadratics will not factorise.

To show that $x - h$ is a factor of $f(x)$, you need to show that $f(h) = 0$.

Example 2: If $f(x) = x^4 + x^3 - 3x^2 - 4x - 4$, show that $x - 2$ is a factor of $f(x)$ and hence factorise $f(x)$ completely.

$f(2) = 2^4 + 2^3 - 3 \times 2^2 - 4 \times 2 - 4 = 0$ so **$x - 2$ is a factor of $f(x)$.**

2	1	1	−3	−4	−4
		2	6	6	4
−2	1	3	3	2	0
		−2	−2	−2	
	1	1	1	0	

$$x^4 + x^3 - 3x^2 - 4x - 4$$
$$= (x-2)(x^3 + 3x^2 + 3x + 2)$$
$$= \mathbf{(x-2)(x+2)(x^2 + x + 1)}$$

$x^2 + x + 1$ does not factorise.

In some examples it may be necessary to try fraction values of h to find a factor.

In this case it can help to consider graphical ideas. The x-axis intercepts of the graph of $y = f(x)$ will give the solutions to the equation $f(x) = 0$.

Looking at the graph of $y = f(x)$ on a graphic calculator or in a sketch can help find a value for h to factorise $f(x)$ (see Example 3 below) or to find the solutions to the equation $f(x) = 0$ (see Section 2.1.6).

Example 3: Factorise completely $f(x) = 12x^3 - 28x^2 - 9x + 10$.

It can help to use the graphic calculator here. It appears that the curve $y = f(x)$ cuts the x-axis at $\frac{1}{2}$.

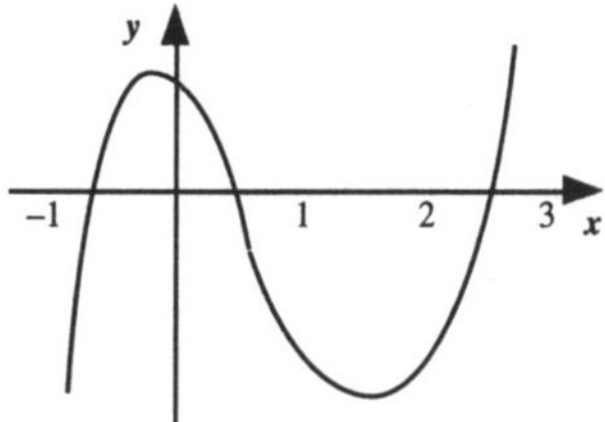

Try $h = \frac{1}{2}$.

$\frac{1}{2}$	12	−28	−9	10
		6	−11	−10
	12	−22	−20	0

$$12x^3 - 28x^2 - 9x + 10$$
$$= (x - \tfrac{1}{2})(12x^2 - 22x - 20)$$
$$= (x - \tfrac{1}{2})2(6x^2 - 11x - 10)$$
$$= 2(x - \tfrac{1}{2})(2x - 5)(3x + 2)$$
$$= \mathbf{(2x-1)(2x-5)(3x+2)}$$

2.1.6 Solving Polynomial Equations by Factorising

If $f(x)$ is a polynomial and $f(h) = 0$, then h is called a **root** of the equation $f(x) = 0$.

To solve a polynomial equation, you should first try to factorise the polynomial using the Factor Theorem, and then equate each factor to zero.

Example: Determine the roots of the equation $2x^3 - 7x^2 - 17x + 10 = 0$.

$$\begin{array}{r|rrrr} -2 & 2 & -7 & -17 & 10 \\ & & -4 & 22 & -10 \\ \hline & 2 & -11 & 5 & 0 \end{array}$$

$$2x^3 - 7x^2 - 17x + 10 = 0$$
$$(x+2)(2x^2 - 11x + 5) = 0$$
$$(x+2)(x-5)(2x-1) = 0$$
$$x+2=0 \quad \text{or} \quad x-5=0 \quad \text{or} \quad 2x-1=0$$
$$x = \mathbf{-2} \qquad x = \mathbf{5} \qquad x = \tfrac{\mathbf{1}}{\mathbf{2}}$$

The solutions to polynomial equations can also be found by graphing. However if the question asks you to solve **algebraically**, then you must use this method.

2.1.7 Solving Equations by Numerical Methods

It is not always possible, or practical, to factorise $f(x)$ in the equation $f(x) = 0$. In such cases, you can find a numerical solution using the following method which you met in Standard Grade.

1. Identify an approximate solution - often by checking it lies between two values.
2. Choose new values which repeatedly home in on the root until the required degree of accuracy has been reached.

A repetitive process like this is known as an **iterative process**, or **iteration**.

Proving that a Root Lies Between Two Given Values

If $f(a)$ and $f(b)$ have different signs, eg
$f(a)$ negative and $f(b)$ positive (as shown)
or $f(a)$ positive and $f(b)$ negative
then there must be a value c, such that $a < c < b$, and $f(c) = 0$, ie c is a root of $f(x) = 0$.

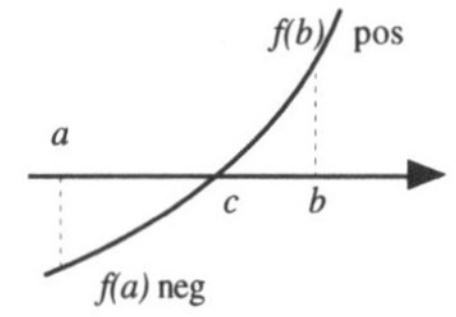

To prove that there is a root between two given x values therefore, you need to show that these x values give different signs for $f(x)$ (see the following example).

Improving the Solution by Iteration

1. Choose a value d between a and b and evaluate $f(d)$, noting whether the value obtained is positive or negative.
2. Repeat this for other values which 'sandwich' the actual root more closely, until the desired accuracy has been obtained. It is often helpful to halve the interval between the last two approximations. Record the values in a table.

Example: Show that the equation $x^3 - 5x^2 + 2x + 5 = 0$ has a root between –1 and 0 and find it correct to 2 decimal places.

$$f(x) = x^3 - 5x^2 + 2x + 5$$
$$f(-1) = (-1)^3 - 5\times(-1)^2 + 2\times(-1) + 5 = -3$$
$$f(0) = 0^3 - 5\times 0^2 + 2\times 0 + 5 = 5$$

$f(-1)$ and $f(0)$ have different signs, therefore **there is a root between -1 and 0.**

$$f(x) = x^3 - 5x^2 + 2x + 5$$
$$f(-0.5) = 2.625$$
$$f(-0.7) = 0.807$$
$$f(-0.8) = -0.312$$
$$f(-0.75) = 0.265...$$
$$f(-0.77) = 0.038...$$
$$f(-0.78) = -0.076...$$
$$f(-0.775) = -0.018...$$

x values f(x) neg	x values f(x) pos
–1	0
–0.8	–0.5
–0.78	–0.7
–0.775	–0.75
	–0.77

The root lies between –0.77 and –0.775, so $f(x) = 0$ has a root **–0.77** to 2dp.

2.1.8 Quadratics

A polynomial of degree 2 is called a **quadratic**. A quadratic expression will have the form $ax^2 + bx + c$.

In Standard Grade you have met quadratic expressions, functions and equations, and learnt how to factorise a quadratic expression. This will be revised briefly here.

2.1.9 Factorising Quadratics

When factorising, you should look for factors in the following order.

> **1. A Common Factor**
>
> **2. A Difference of Two Squares**
>
> **3. A Pair of Brackets**

Watch for more than one type of factor being present, eg a common factor then a difference of squares, or a difference of squares twice.

An expression is not regarded as fully factorised until all possible factorisation has been completed.

Example 1:

$2x^3 - 18xy^2$

$= 2x(x^2 - 9y^2)$

$= \mathbf{2x(x - 3y)(x + 3y)}$

Example 2:

$x^4 - 1$

$= (x^2 - 1)(x^2 + 1)$

$= \mathbf{(x - 1)(x + 1)(x^2 + 1)}$

Example 3:

$30x^2 - 75x - 45$

$= 15(2x^2 - 5x - 3)$

$= \mathbf{15(2x + 1)(x - 3)}$

2.1.10 Quadratic Equations

All **quadratic equations** can be written in the **standard form**:

$$\mathbf{ax^2 + bx + c = 0} \qquad (a \neq 0)$$

> **To solve a quadratic equation, first try factorising.**
>
> **If the equation does not factorise, try the formula.**

If the equation can factorise, the solutions will be integral or rational.

The formula will usually give irrational roots. These must be rounded or left as exact values using surds.

Solving by Factorising

1. Arrange the equation into the standard form with the right hand side equal to 0.
2. Factorise the quadratic expression on the left hand side.
3. This will result in simple linear equations which can be solved the usual way.

Example 1:

$$2x^2 + x = 6$$
$$2x^2 + x - 6 = 0$$
$$(2x-3)(x+2) = 0$$
$$2x - 3 = 0 \quad \text{or} \quad x + 2 = 0$$
$$2x = 3 \qquad\qquad \boldsymbol{x = -2}$$
$$\boldsymbol{x = \tfrac{3}{2}}$$

Example 2:

$$x - 1 = \frac{2}{x}$$

Multiply by x

$$x^2 - x = 2$$
$$x^2 - x - 2 = 0$$
$$(x-2)(x+1) = 0$$
$$x - 2 = 0 \quad \text{or} \quad x + 1 = 0$$
$$\boldsymbol{x = 2} \qquad\qquad \boldsymbol{x = -1}$$

Solving by Formula

If a quadratic equation cannot factorise, you can try to solve it by using the **quadratic formula**:

If $\boldsymbol{ax^2 + bx + c = 0}$, $(a \neq 0)$ then

$$\boldsymbol{x = \frac{-b \pm \sqrt{b^2 - 4ac}}{2a}}.$$

1. Arrange into the standard form with the right hand side equal to 0.
2. Substitute the values for a, b and c into the formula.

Example 1:

$$x^2+6x+1=0$$

$a=1 \quad b=6 \quad c=1$

$$x=\frac{-b\pm\sqrt{b^2-4ac}}{2a}$$

$$x=\frac{-6\pm\sqrt{6^2-4\times1\times1}}{2\times1}$$

$$x=\frac{-6\pm\sqrt{36-4}}{2}$$

$x=\dfrac{-6+\sqrt{32}}{2}$ or $x=\dfrac{-6-\sqrt{32}}{2}$

$x=\dfrac{-6+4\sqrt{2}}{2}$ $\quad x=\dfrac{-6-4\sqrt{2}}{2}$

$x=\mathbf{-3+2\sqrt{2}}$ $\quad x=\mathbf{-3-2\sqrt{2}}$

These are the exact values of the solutions.

Note : $\sqrt{32}=\sqrt{16\times2}=\sqrt{16}\times\sqrt{2}=4\sqrt{2}$

(See Standard Grade for use of surds.)

Example 2:

$$x^2-4=5x$$

$$x^2-5x-4=0$$

$a=1 \quad b=-5 \quad c=-4$

$$x=\frac{-b\pm\sqrt{b^2-4ac}}{2a}$$

$$x=\frac{-(-5)\pm\sqrt{(-5)^2-4\times1\times(-4)}}{2\times1}$$

$$x=\frac{5\pm\sqrt{25+16}}{2}$$

$x=\dfrac{5+\sqrt{41}}{2}$ or $x=\dfrac{5-\sqrt{41}}{2}$

$x=5.701...$ $\quad x=-0.701...$

$x=\mathbf{5.7}$ $\quad x=\mathbf{-0.7}$ to 1 dp

These are approximate values of the solutions.

2.1.11 The Discriminant

When using the formula to solve a quadratic equation, it is the value inside the square root sign that will determine whether there will be roots, and if so, what type.

For the quadratic equation $ax^2+bx+c=0$, you call the expression b^2-4ac the **discriminant**. The following table summarises how it determines the type of roots.

Discrimant Value	Roots are:	
$b^2-4ac=0$	real	equal (1 root)
$b^2-4ac>0$	real	distinct (2 roots)
$b^2-4ac<0$	not real	(0 roots)

This can be used in two ways - either

given the nature of the roots for a particular equation, to find the condition that makes this happen (see Example 1),

or

to find out the nature of the roots of a particular equation (see Example 2).

Example 1: For what values of k does the equation
(a) $x^2 + kx + 9 = 0$ have equal roots,
(b) $5x^2 - 2x + k = 0$ have real roots?

(a) $x^2 + kx + 9 = 0$

$a = 1 \quad b = k \quad c = 9$

For equal roots, $disc = 0$

$$b^2 - 4ac = 0$$
$$(k)^2 - 4 \times 1 \times 9 = 0$$
$$k^2 - 36 = 0$$
$$(k-6)(k+6) = 0$$
$$k - 6 = 0 \quad \text{or} \quad k + 6 = 0$$
$$k = \mathbf{6} \qquad k = \mathbf{-6}$$

(b) $5x^2 - 2x + k = 0$

$a = 5 \quad b = -2 \quad c = k$

For real roots, $disc \geq 0$

$$b^2 - 4ac \geq 0$$
$$(-2)^2 - 4 \times 5 \times k \geq 0$$
$$4 - 20k \geq 0$$
$$-20k \geq -4$$
$$20k \leq 4$$
$$k \leq \mathbf{\tfrac{1}{5}}$$

Example 2: Show that the equation
(a) $qx^2 + px - q = 0$, where $q \neq 0$, has real roots,
(b) $\cos^2 x - 4\cos x + 5 = 0$ has no real roots.

(a) $qx^2 + px - q = 0$

$a = q \quad b = p \quad c = -q$

$$\begin{aligned} disc &= b^2 - 4ac \\ &= (p)^2 - 4 \times q \times (-q) \\ &= p^2 + 4q^2 \\ &> 0 \end{aligned}$$

(***the sum of two squares***)

It has **real roots**.

(b) $\cos^2 x - 4\cos x + 5 = 0$

This is a quadratic in $\mathbf{\cos x}$.

$a = 1 \quad b = -4 \quad c = 5$

$$\begin{aligned} disc &= b^2 - 4ac \\ &= (-4)^2 - 4 \times 1 \times 5 \\ &= -4 \\ &< 0 \end{aligned}$$

It has **no real roots**.

2.1.12 The Intersection of a Line and a Curve

When a straight line meets a parabola, it will intersect it in either two points, in one point if it is a **tangent**, or it will not intersect it at all.

For other curves, the same choice will occur in a local area, but the line may then cut the curve again elsewhere.

An **intersection equation** can be formed from the equations of the line and the curve. If the intersection equation is quadratic, you can use its discriminant to determine how the line cuts the curve.

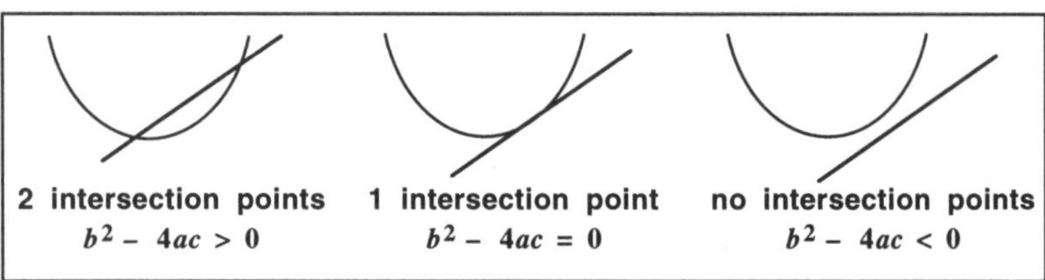

1. Set up the intersection equation either by equating the equations of the straight line and the curve, or by substituting the straight line equation into the curve equation.

2. Use the discriminant to find the nature of the intersection points.

3. If you require to find the actual intersection points, solve the intersection equation to find the x-coordinates and substitute these into the straight line equation to find the y-coordinates. Sometimes it may be easier to find the y-coordinates first.

Example 1: For what values of m is the line with equation $y = mx - 1$ a tangent to the parabola with equation $y = x^2 + 2x + 3$?

$y_1 = x^2 + 2x + 3 \qquad y_2 = mx - 1$

Intersection Equation: $y_1 = y_2$

$$x^2 + 2x + 3 = mx - 1$$

$$x^2 + 2x - mx + 3 + 1 = 0$$

$$x^2 + (2 - m)x + 4 = 0$$

$a = 1 \qquad b = 2 - m \qquad c = 4$

For equal roots $\quad disc = 0$

$$b^2 - 4ac = 0$$
$$(2-m)^2 - 4\times1\times4 = 0$$
$$4 - 4m + m^2 - 16 = 0$$
$$m^2 - 4m - 12 = 0$$
$$(m-6)(m+2) = 0$$
$$m - 6 = 0 \quad \text{or} \quad m + 2 = 0$$
$$m = 6 \qquad\qquad m = -2$$

The line will be a tangent when $m = \mathbf{6}$ or $m = \mathbf{-2}$.

Example 2: Show that the line with equation $y = 3x - 3$ is a tangent to the curve with equation $y = 2x^2 - 5x + 5$.
Find algebraically the coordinates of the point of contact.

$y_1 = 2x^2 - 5x + 5 \qquad y_2 = 3x - 3$

Intersection Equation: $\quad y_1 = y_2$

$$2x^2 - 5x + 5 = 3x - 3$$
$$2x^2 - 5x + 5 - 3x + 3 = 0$$
$$2x^2 - 8x + 8 = 0$$
$$2(x^2 - 4x + 4) = 0$$
$$2(x-2)(x-2) = 0$$
$$x - 2 = 0 \quad \text{or} \quad x - 2 = 0$$
$$x = 2 \qquad\qquad x = 2$$

You could use the discriminant at this point to show it is a tangent.

However since you need to find the point of contact in any case, you can just continue to solve the intersection equation.

Since the intersection equation has equal roots, **the line is a tangent**.

$$x = 2 \qquad y_2 = 3x - 3$$
$$= 3\times2 - 3$$
$$= 3$$

The point of contact has coordinates $(\mathbf{2,3})$.

2.1.13 Quadratic Inequations

All **quadratic inequations** can be written in the **standard form**:

$$ax^2 + bx + c \le 0 \qquad (a \ne 0)$$

(or using <, >, ≥)

To solve a quadratic inequation:

1. Sketch the equivalent function $y = ax^2 + bx + c$, identifying the zeros (see Section 1.2.9).
2. Use the sketch to decide on which intervals the function will be greater / less than 0. $f(x) > 0$ (< 0) where the curve is above (below) the x-axis. Remember to check whether the zeros are included.
3. Give the solution as one or two intervals of x values.

Example: Solve the inequations
(a) $x^2 + x - 2 \le 0$ (b) $x^2 + x - 2 > 0$.

Since the x^2 term is positive, it will be a U-shaped parabola.

<u>x-axis intercepts:</u>

Solve

$$\begin{aligned} y &= 0 \\ x^2 + x - 2 &= 0 \\ (x+2)(x-1) &= 0 \end{aligned}$$

$$x + 2 = 0 \quad \text{or} \quad x - 1 = 0$$

$$x = -2 \qquad\qquad x = 1$$

The x-axis intercepts are $(-2,0)$ and $(1,0)$.

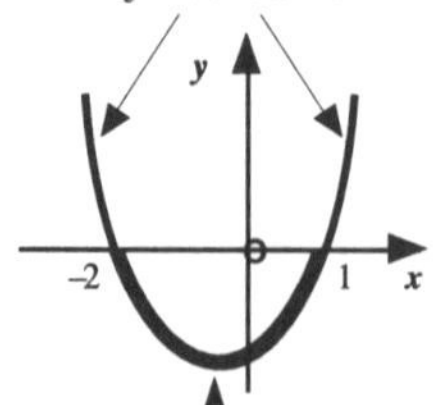

(a) The curve is below the x-axis between the zeros, so
$x^2 + x - 2 \le 0$ when $\mathbf{-2 \le x \le 1}$.
(Zeros are included since it is "less than or equal to".)

(b) The curve is above the x-axis outside the zeros, so
$x^2 + x - 2 > 0$ when $\mathbf{x < -2}$ or $\mathbf{x > 1}$.
(Zeros are not included since it is only "greater than".)

2.2 BASIC INTEGRATION

In the Higher course, integration has two main uses:

1. the reverse process to differentiation - the **indefinite integral**,

and

2. a process for finding the areas associated with curves - the **definite integral**.

2.2.1 The Indefinite Integral

The **indefinite integral of** $f(x)$ **with respect to** x is defined to be the function $F(x)$ whose derivative $F'(x) = f(x)$. It is sometimes called the **anti-derivative** of $f(x)$ because of this. It is written:

$$\int f(x)dx$$

The process of finding the integral is called **integration** and to find it you **integrate** the function $f(x)$.

Because the derivative of a constant is zero there are infinitely many functions $F(x)$, differing by a constant, that will all have the same derivative $f(x)$, eg

$$\left.\begin{array}{l} F(x)=x^2 \\ F(x)=x^2+5 \\ F(x)=x^2-10 \end{array}\right\} \qquad f(x)=F'(x)=2x.$$

When $f(x)$ is integrated therefore, you must show a general constant, C, called the **constant of integration**, eg

$$f(x)=2x \qquad \int f(x)\,dx = x^2 + C.$$

2.2.2 The Rules for Integrating

The rules for integrating are derived from the rules for differentiating.
The basic rule allows you to integrate powers of x, where $n \neq -1$.

$$\boxed{f(x)=x^n \rightarrow \int f(x)dx = \frac{x^{n+1}}{n+1}+C \qquad (n \neq -1)}$$

Mathematics 2.2: Basic Integration

Example 1:

$$f(x)=x^5$$
$$\int f(x)dx=\frac{x^6}{6}+C$$
$$=\tfrac{1}{6}x^6+C$$

Example 2:

$$f(x)=x^{-3}$$
$$\int f(x)dx=\frac{x^{-2}}{-2}+C$$
$$=-\tfrac{1}{2}x^{-2}+C$$

Example 3:

$$f(x)=x^{\frac{1}{2}}$$
$$\int f(x)dx=\frac{1}{3/2}x^{\frac{3}{2}}+C$$
$$=\tfrac{2}{3}x^{\frac{3}{2}}+C$$

This can be extended to multiples and sums or differences of powers of x.

$f(x)=ax^n$	$\rightarrow$	$\int ax^n dx=\frac{ax^{n+1}}{n+1}+C$	$(n\neq -1)$
$f(x)=ax^n+bx^m$	$\rightarrow$	$\int\left(ax^n+bx^m\right)dx=\frac{ax^{n+1}}{n+1}+\frac{bx^{m+1}}{m+1}+C$	$(n,m\neq -1)$

Example 4:

$$f(x)=5x^4$$
$$\int f(x)dx=\frac{5x^5}{5}+C$$
$$=x^5+C$$

Example 5:

$$f(x)=\tfrac{3}{4}x^{-\frac{1}{2}}$$
$$\int f(x)dx=\frac{\frac{3}{4}x^{\frac{1}{2}}}{\frac{1}{2}}+C$$
$$=\tfrac{3}{2}x^{\frac{1}{2}}+C$$

Example 6:

$$f(x)=2x^3-3x+5$$
$$\int f(x)dx=\frac{2x^4}{4}-\frac{3x^2}{2}+5x+C$$
$$=\tfrac{1}{2}x^4-\tfrac{3}{2}x^2+5x+C$$

As for differentiation, any brackets must first be multiplied out until you have a sum or difference of powers of x, and then integrate.

Example 7:

$$f(x)=(x-3)(x+2)$$
$$=x^2-x-6$$
$$\int f(x)dx=\frac{x^3}{3}-\frac{x^2}{2}-6x+C$$
$$=\tfrac{1}{3}x^3-\tfrac{1}{2}x^2-6x+C$$

Example 8:

$$f(x)=(2x-3)^2$$
$$=4x^2-12x+9$$
$$\int f(x)dx=\frac{4x^3}{3}-\frac{12x^2}{2}+9x+C$$
$$=\tfrac{4}{3}x^3-6x^2+9x+C$$

2.2.3 Using the Integration Rules - Harder Examples

As for differentiation, you will need to use the index rules to change into a suitable form for integrating. You may also want to change your answer.

1. First use the index definitions and rules to get the function ready for integrating.
2. Use the integration rules to find the integral.
3. If necessary, use the index definitions and rules to change the form of the answer.

Example 1:

$$\begin{aligned} f(x) &= 6x^2 - \frac{3}{2x^2} \\ &= 6x^2 - \tfrac{3}{2}x^{-2} \\ \int f(x)\,dx &= \frac{6x^3}{3} - \frac{\tfrac{3}{2}x^{-1}}{-1} + C \\ &= 2x^3 + \tfrac{3}{2}x^{-1} + C \\ &= \mathbf{2x^3 + \frac{3}{2x} + C} \end{aligned}$$

This answer would be acceptable (refers to $= 2x^3 + \tfrac{3}{2}x^{-1} + C$)

Example 2:

$$\begin{aligned} f(x) &= \sqrt{x}\left(\sqrt{x} - \frac{1}{\sqrt{x}}\right) \\ &= x^{\frac{1}{2}}\left(x^{\frac{1}{2}} - x^{-\frac{1}{2}}\right) \\ &= x^{\frac{1}{2}+\frac{1}{2}} - x^{\frac{1}{2}-\frac{1}{2}} \\ &= x - 1 \\ \int f(x)\,dx &= \frac{x^2}{2} - x + C \\ &= \mathbf{\tfrac{1}{2}x^2 - x + C} \end{aligned}$$

Example 3:

$$\begin{aligned} f(x) &= \frac{2x^2 - x}{5\sqrt{x}} \\ &= \tfrac{1}{5}x^{-\frac{1}{2}}\left(2x^2 - x\right) \\ &= \tfrac{1}{5}x^{-\frac{1}{2}} \times 2x^2 - \tfrac{1}{5}x^{-\frac{1}{2}} \times x^1 \\ &= \tfrac{1}{5} \times 2 \times x^{-\frac{1}{2}+2} - \tfrac{1}{5}x^{-\frac{1}{2}+1} \\ &= \tfrac{2}{5}x^{\frac{3}{2}} - \tfrac{1}{5}x^{\frac{1}{2}} \end{aligned}$$

$$\begin{aligned} \int f(x)\,dx &= \frac{\tfrac{2}{5}x^{\frac{5}{2}}}{\tfrac{5}{2}} - \frac{\tfrac{1}{5}x^{\frac{3}{2}}}{\tfrac{3}{2}} + C \\ &= \mathbf{\tfrac{4}{25}x^{\frac{5}{2}} - \tfrac{2}{15}x^{\frac{3}{2}} + C} \end{aligned}$$

2.2.4 Using the Indefinite Integral - Differential Equations

The indefinite integral is used in any situation where the reverse process to differentiation is required.

An equation involving $\frac{dy}{dx}$ or $f'(x)$ is called a **differential equation**.
To solve it, you must find a suitable function y or $f(x)$ which would have $\frac{dy}{dx}$ or $f'(x)$ as its derivative.

1. Integrate the differential equation to find y or $f(x)$. The integral will include the constant of integration C, and is called the **general solution** of the differential equation.

2. Use further information given in the question to find the value of C. The integral with this value for C is called the **particular solution** of the differential equation.

Example: $f'(x) = 3x^2 - x - 2$ and $f(-2) = -4$. Find $f(x)$.

$$f'(x) = 3x^2 - x - 2$$
$$f(x) = \int (3x^2 - x - 2)dx$$
$$= \frac{3x^3}{3} - \frac{x^2}{2} - 2x + C$$
$$= x^3 - \tfrac{1}{2}x^2 - 2x + C \quad \longleftarrow \quad \textit{General solution}$$

$$f(-2) = -4$$
$$(-2)^3 - \tfrac{1}{2}(-2)^2 - 2\times(-2) + C = -4$$
$$-6 + C = -4$$
$$C = 2$$

$$\boldsymbol{f(x) = x^3 - \tfrac{1}{2}x^2 - 2x + 2} \quad \longleftarrow \quad \textit{Particular solution}$$

2.2.5 Finding the Equation of a Curve Given the Gradient and a Point on the Curve

The context for solving a differential equation is often curve sketching. In this case, you will be given the formula for the gradient of the curve and a point on it. You are required to find the equation of the curve.

Example: The curve $y = f(x)$ passes through the point $(3, -1)$ and $f'(x) = (x-3)^2$. Find $f(x)$.

$$f'(x) = (x-3)^2$$
$$= x^2 - 6x + 9$$
$$f(x) = \int\left(x^2 - 6x + 9\right)dx$$
$$= \frac{x^3}{3} - \frac{6x^2}{2} + 9x + C$$
$$= \tfrac{1}{3}x^3 - 3x^2 + 9x + C$$

$$y = f(x)$$
$y = -1$ when $x = 3$
$$-1 = \tfrac{1}{3}\times 3^3 - 3\times 3^2 + 9\times 3 + C$$
$$-1 = 9 + C$$
$$C = -10$$
$$\mathbf{f(x) = \tfrac{1}{3}x^3 - 3x^2 + 9x - 10}$$

2.2.6 Using Integration with Distance, Speed and Acceleration

In Section 1.3.11, you learned that speed is the derivative of distance and acceleration is the derivative of speed with respect to time. You can use integration therefore to find distance from speed or speed from acceleration.

acceleration	a
speed	$v = \int a\,dt$
distance	$s = \int v\,dt$

Example: A car is driving at 15 m/s. As it passes a post, it starts to accelerate at $4t$ m/s^2, where t is the number of seconds after passing the post. What will its speed be 3 seconds after passing the post?

acceleration $a = 4t$

speed
$$v = \int a\,dt$$
$$= \int 4t\,dt$$
$$= \frac{4t^2}{2} + C$$
$$v = 2t^2 + C$$

$t = 0 \quad v = 15$
$$15 = 2\times 0^2 + C$$
$$C = 15$$
$$v = 2t^2 + 15$$

$t = 3$
$$v = 2\times 3^2 + 15$$
$$= 33$$

Its speed will be **33 m/s**.

2.2.7 The Definite Integral

The **definite integral of $f(x)$ with respect to x from $x = a$ to $x = b$** is defined to be

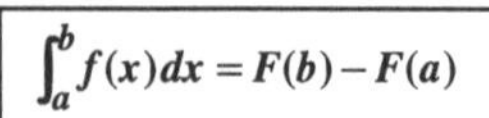

$$\int_a^b f(x)dx = F(b) - F(a)$$

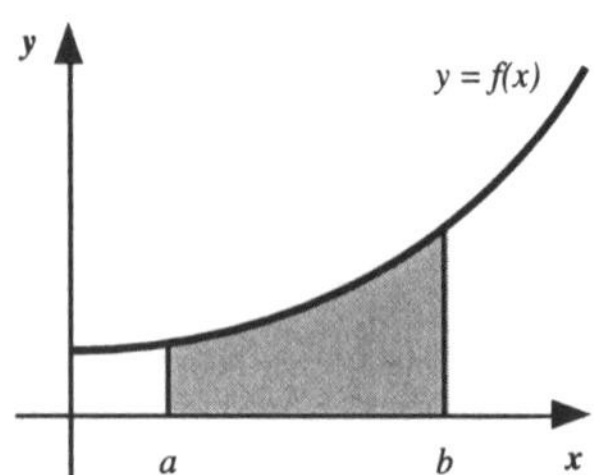

where $F(x)$ is the function whose derivative $F'(x) = f(x)$.

In simple cases, the value obtained is the **area under the curve $f(x)$**, shown shaded.

a and b are called the **limits of integration**. a is called the **lower limit of integration** and b is called the **upper limit of integration**.

The same rules are used to find $F(x)$ as for the indefinite integral.
However, you do not include the constant of integration in a definite integral.

Example 1:

$$\int_1^2 x^3\,dx = \left[\frac{x^4}{4}\right]_1^2$$
$$= \left(\frac{2^4}{4}\right) - \left(\frac{1^4}{4}\right)$$
$$= 4 - \tfrac{1}{4}$$
$$= \mathbf{3\tfrac{3}{4}}$$

Example 2:

$$\int_{-1}^4 (3x-2)\,dx = \left[\frac{3x^2}{2} - 2x\right]_{-1}^4$$
$$= \left(\frac{3\times 4^2}{2} - 2\times 4\right) - \left(\frac{3\times(-1)^2}{2} - 2\times(-1)\right)$$
$$= 24 - 8 - \tfrac{3}{2} - 2$$
$$= \mathbf{12\tfrac{1}{2}}$$

Harder examples are completed as for indefinite integrals (see Section 2.2.3). You use the index definitions and rules first to prepare for integrating. It is often helpful to change the intregrated form back to fractions, positive powers and roots before substituting the limits into it.

Example 3:

$$\int_1^9\left(\sqrt{x}-\frac{3}{x^2}\right)dx$$

$$=\int_1^9\left(x^{\frac{1}{2}}-3x^{-2}\right)dx$$

$$=\left[\frac{x^{\frac{3}{2}}}{\frac{3}{2}}-\frac{3x^{-1}}{-1}\right]_1^9$$

$$=\left[\frac{2x^{\frac{3}{2}}}{3}+\frac{3}{x}\right]_1^9$$

$$=\left(\frac{2\times 9^{\frac{3}{2}}}{3}+\frac{3}{9}\right)-\left(\frac{2\times 1^{\frac{3}{2}}}{3}+\frac{3}{1}\right)$$

$$=18+\tfrac{1}{3}-\tfrac{2}{3}-3$$

$$=\mathbf{14\tfrac{2}{3}}$$

When evaluating a definite integral without having access to a calculator, it may be more helpful to use roots instead of fractional indices as below.

$$=\left[\frac{2\left(\sqrt{x}\right)^3}{3}+\frac{3}{x}\right]_1^9$$

$$=\left(\frac{2\left(\sqrt{9}\right)^3}{3}+\frac{3}{9}\right)-\left(\frac{2\left(\sqrt{1}\right)^3}{3}+\frac{3}{1}\right)$$

2.2.8 Area Under a Curve

The definite integral can be used to find areas associated with curves.

You must remember that where the curve $f(x)$ lies below the x-axis, the definite integral will give a negative value.

In particular:

1. When $f(x) \geq 0$, the shaded area between the curve and the x-axis from $x = a$ to $x = b$ will be given by:

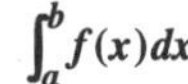

$$\int_a^b f(x)\,dx$$

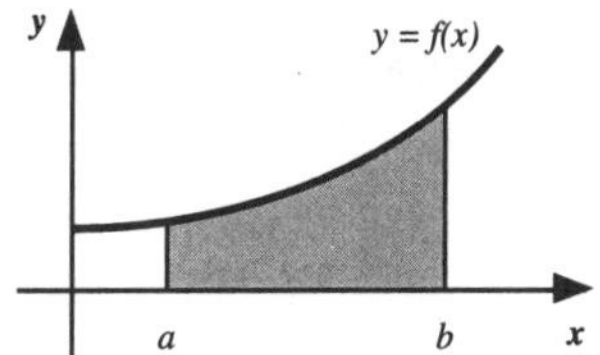

2. When $f(x) \leq 0$, the shaded area between the curve and the x-axis from $x = a$ to $x = b$ will be given by:

$$-\int_a^b f(x)dx$$

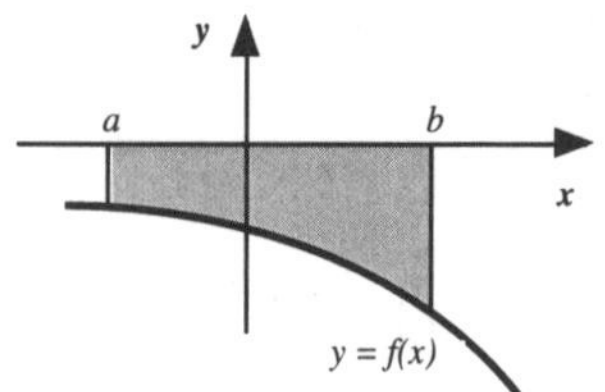

3. When the curve crosses the x-axis at a point c between a and b, the shaded area between the curve and the x-axis from $x = a$ to $x = b$ must be split into two parts.

   In the example illustrated, the area below the axis from a to c and the area above the axis from c to b must be integrated separately.

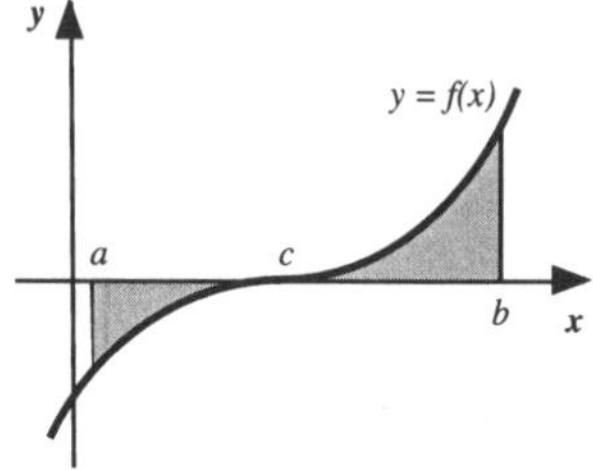

   The area (in this case) will be given by:

$$-\int_a^c f(x)dx + \int_c^b f(x)dx$$

To find the area:

1. Sketch the curve to check whether it cuts the x-axis in between the end points. You may have to find the end points and/or any intersections with the x-axis algebraically by solving an equation.

2. Use integration to find the area, treating parts above and below the axis separately if necessary.

Example 1: Find the area enclosed by the curve $y = 5x - x^2$ and the x-axis.

Intersections with x-axis:

$$5x - x^2 = 0$$
$$x(5 - x) = 0$$
$$x = 0 \quad \text{or} \quad 5 - x = 0$$
$$x = 5$$

Intersects x-axis at (0,0) and (5,0).

x^2 term negative - upside down U-shaped parabola.

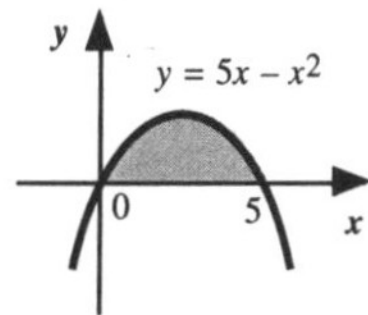

Required area is above the x-axis from $x = 0$ to $x = 5$.

$$\int_0^5 \left(5x - x^2\right)dx = \left[\frac{5x^2}{2} - \frac{x^3}{3}\right]_0^5$$
$$= \left(\frac{5 \times 5^2}{2} - \frac{5^3}{3}\right) - (0 - 0)$$
$$= \tfrac{125}{2} - \tfrac{125}{3}$$
$$= \tfrac{125}{6}$$

$$\text{Area} = \int_0^5 \left(5x - x^2\right)dx$$
$$= \mathbf{\tfrac{125}{6}} \quad \left(= \mathbf{20\tfrac{5}{6}}\right)$$

Example 2: The River Deep - Mountain High outdoor pursuits club are wanting a new logo.
A graphic designer uses the two regions enclosed by the function $y = x^3 - 4x^2 - 4x + 16$ and the x-axis to model it.
Find the area of the logo.

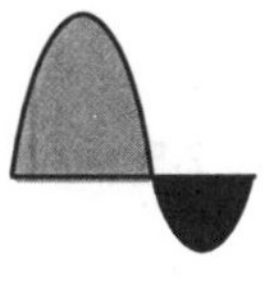

To sketch the curve, find the intersections with the x-axis algebraically. Use the methods from Section 2.1.5 to factorise the cubic. You can then use the most powerful term, x^3, to decide how the cubic will lie, or check it out on a graphic calculator.

Intersections with x-axis:

$$x^3 - 4x^2 - 4x + 16 = 0$$
$$(x + 2)(x - 2)(x - 4) = 0$$
$$x + 2 = 0 \quad \text{or} \quad x - 2 = 0 \quad \text{or} \quad x - 4 = 0$$
$$x = -2 \qquad x = 2 \qquad x = 4$$

Intersects x-axis at (–2,0), (2,0) and (4,0).

Integrate from –2 to 2 and from 2 to 4 separately.

$$\int_{-2}^{2}\left(x^3-4x^2-4x+16\right)dx$$
$$=\left[\frac{x^4}{4}-\frac{4x^3}{3}-\frac{4x^2}{2}+16x\right]_{-2}^{2}$$
$$=\left(\frac{2^4}{4}-\frac{4\times2^3}{3}-\frac{4\times2^2}{2}+16\times2\right)$$
$$-\left(\frac{(-2)^4}{4}-\frac{4\times(-2)^3}{3}-\frac{4\times(-2)^2}{2}+16\times(-2)\right)$$
$$=\left(4-\tfrac{32}{3}-8+32\right)$$
$$-\left(4+\tfrac{32}{3}-8-32\right)$$
$$=-\tfrac{64}{3}+64$$
$$=42\tfrac{2}{3}$$

$$\int_{2}^{4}\left(x^3-4x^2-4x+16\right)dx$$
$$=\left[\frac{x^4}{4}-\frac{4x^3}{3}-\frac{4x^2}{2}+16x\right]_{2}^{4}$$
$$=\left(\frac{4^4}{4}-\frac{4\times4^3}{3}-\frac{4\times4^2}{2}+16\times4\right)$$
$$-\left(\frac{2^4}{4}-\frac{4\times2^3}{3}-\frac{4\times2^2}{2}+16\times2\right)$$
$$=\left(64-\tfrac{256}{3}-32+64\right)$$
$$-\left(4-\tfrac{32}{3}-8+32\right)$$
$$=10\tfrac{2}{3}-17\tfrac{1}{3}$$
$$=-6\tfrac{2}{3}$$

$$\text{Area}=\int_{-2}^{2}\left(x^3-4x^2-4x+16\right)dx+\left(-\int_{2}^{4}\left(x^3-4x^2-4x+16\right)dx\right)$$
$$=42\tfrac{2}{3}+\left(-(-6\tfrac{2}{3})\right)$$
$$=\mathbf{49\tfrac{1}{3}}$$

2.2.9 Area Between Curves

When an area is bounded above and below by curves, you can find the area directly.

If $f(x)\geq g(x)$, for $a\leq x\leq b$, the shaded area between the curves from $x=a$ to $x=b$ will be given by

$$\int_a^b (f(x)-g(x))dx$$

where $y=f(x)$ is the top curve and $y=g(x)$ is the bottom curve.

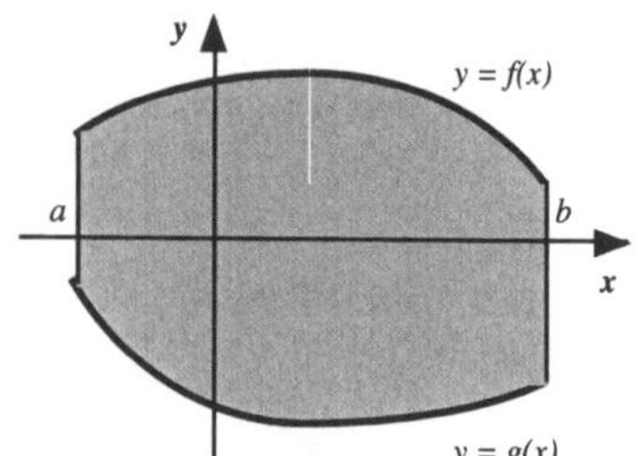

It will usually ease the integration if you simplify $f(x)-g(x)$ before integrating.

Note: There is no problem if either or both curves cross the x-axis.

If the two curves cross over and $f(x)$ goes below $g(x)$, the definite integral would give a negative value. In this case you must integrate the two parts separately.

When the curves cross each other at a point with $x = c$ where $a < c < b$, the shaded area between the curves from $x = a$ to $x = b$ must be split into two parts.

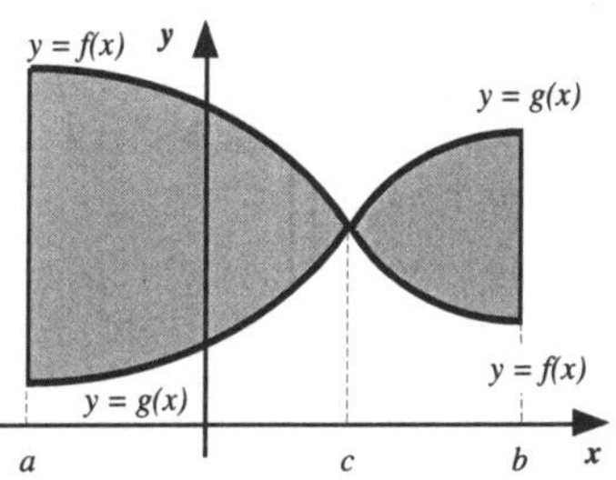

In the example illustrated, the area from a to c must be found by integrating with $f(x)$ as the top function. The area from c to b must be found by integrating with $g(x)$ as the top function.

The area (in this case) will be given by:

$$\int_a^c (f(x) - g(x))dx + \int_c^b (g(x) - f(x))dx$$

Example: Find the area enclosed by the parabolas $y = x^2$ and $y = 8 - x^2$.

Top function: $f(x) = 8 - x^2$

Bottom function: $g(x) = x^2$

Sketch the graphs of the functions. Use the intersection equation to find the x values of the intersection points.

Intersection equation:

$$f(x) = g(x)$$
$$8 - x^2 = x^2$$
$$8 - 2x^2 = 0$$
$$2(4 - x^2) = 0$$
$$2(2 - x)(2 + x) = 0$$
$$x = 2 \quad \text{or} \quad x = -2$$

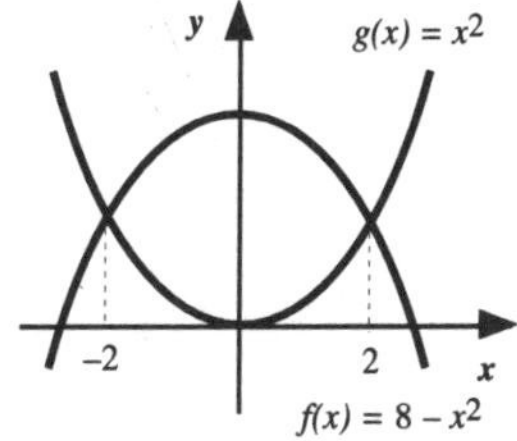

Integrate $f(x) - g(x)$ from $x = -2$ to $x = 2$ to find the enclosed area.

$$\int_{-2}^{2} (f(x) - g(x))dx$$
$$= \int_{-2}^{2} \left(8 - x^2 - x^2\right)dx$$
$$= \int_{-2}^{2} \left(8 - 2x^2\right)dx$$
$$= \left[8x - \frac{2x^3}{3}\right]_{-2}^{2}$$

$$= \left(8 \times 2 - \frac{2 \times 2^3}{3}\right) - \left(8 \times (-2) - \frac{2 \times (-2)^3}{3}\right)$$
$$= 16 - \tfrac{16}{3} - \left(-16 + \tfrac{16}{3}\right)$$
$$= \mathbf{21\tfrac{1}{3}}$$

2.3 TRIGONOMETRIC FORMULAE AND EQUATIONS

2.3.1 Trigonometric Identities

An **identity** is a equation which is true for all values of the variable. The following trig identities are very important in Higher maths.

$$\cos^2 x + \sin^2 x = 1 \qquad\qquad \tan x = \frac{\sin x}{\cos x}$$

You write $\sin^2 x$ to mean $(\sin x)^2$.

These identities can be used to find the **exact values** of the other trig functions when you know the value of one of them (see Section 0.4 for exact values).

Example 1: If $\sin x = \frac{2}{3}$, and $0 < x < \frac{\pi}{2}$, find the exact value of $\cos x$ and $\tan x$.

$$\begin{aligned}
\cos^2 x + \sin^2 x &= 1 \\
\cos^2 x + \left(\tfrac{2}{3}\right)^2 &= 1 \\
\cos^2 x + \tfrac{4}{9} &= 1 \\
\cos^2 x &= 1 - \tfrac{4}{9} \\
\cos^2 x &= \tfrac{5}{9} \\
\cos x &= \pm\sqrt{\tfrac{5}{9}} = \pm\tfrac{\sqrt{5}}{3}
\end{aligned}$$

Since $0 < x < \frac{\pi}{2}$, $\cos x = \frac{\sqrt{5}}{3}$

$$\tan x = \frac{\sin x}{\cos x} = \frac{\frac{2}{3}}{\frac{\sqrt{5}}{3}} = \frac{2}{\sqrt{5}}$$

This type of question can also be completed very easily using a right angled triangle. Since each trig function is a ratio, you can assign the values in the given fraction to the sides of the triangle and use right angled trig.

Example 2: If $\tan x = \frac{3}{5}$, and $0 < x < \frac{\pi}{2}$, find the exact value of $\sin x$ and $\cos x$.

$\tan x = \frac{3}{5}$

Make 3 the opposite and 5 the adjacent.
Use Pythagoras to find the 3rd side.

By Pythagoras' Theorem

$$h^2 = 3^2 + 5^2$$
$$= 34$$
$$h = \sqrt{34}$$

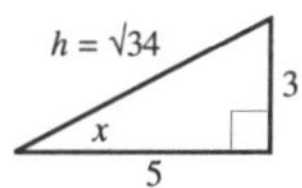

$$\sin x = \frac{o}{h} = \frac{\mathbf{3}}{\sqrt{\mathbf{34}}}$$

$$\cos x = \frac{a}{h} = \frac{\mathbf{5}}{\sqrt{\mathbf{34}}}$$

You can also find the exact values for angles which are not in the first quadrant. Either method can be used. You would assign a negative to the sin, cos or tan values as appropriate, depending on the quadrant being used.

2.3.2 The Addition Formulae

$\cos(A+B) = \cos A\cos B - \sin A\sin B$	$\sin(A+B) = \sin A\cos B + \cos A\sin B$
$\cos(A-B) = \cos A\cos B + \sin A\sin B$	$\sin(A-B) = \sin A\cos B - \cos A\sin B$

Example 1: By expressing $\sin 75°$ as $\sin (45° + 30°)$ find the exact value of $\sin 75°$.

$$\sin 75° = \sin(45°+30°)$$
$$= \sin 45°\cos 30° + \cos 45°\sin 30°$$
$$= \frac{1}{\sqrt{2}} \times \frac{\sqrt{3}}{2} + \frac{1}{\sqrt{2}} \times \frac{1}{2}$$
$$= \frac{\mathbf{\sqrt{3}+1}}{\mathbf{2\sqrt{2}}}$$

Example 2: The diagram shows two right angled triangles with sizes as shown. Show that the exact value of $\cos(x+y)^\circ$ is $\dfrac{5-4\sqrt{5}}{15}$.

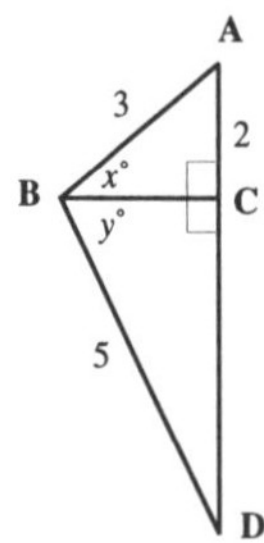

By Pythagoras' Theorem in ΔABC

$$AB^2 = BC^2 + AC^2$$
$$3^2 = BC^2 + 2^2$$
$$BC^2 = 3^2 - 2^2 = 5$$
$$BC = \sqrt{5}$$

By Pythagoras' Theorem in ΔBCD

$$BD^2 = CD^2 + BC^2$$
$$5^2 = CD^2 + \sqrt{5}^2$$
$$CD^2 = 5^2 - 5 = 20$$
$$CD = \sqrt{20} = 2\sqrt{5}$$

$\cos x^\circ = \frac{\sqrt{5}}{3}$ $\quad\sin x^\circ = \frac{2}{3}$

$\cos y^\circ = \frac{\sqrt{5}}{5}$ $\quad\sin y^\circ = \frac{2\sqrt{5}}{5}$

$$\cos(x+y)^\circ = \cos x^\circ \cos y^\circ - \sin x^\circ \sin y^\circ$$
$$= \frac{\sqrt{5}}{3} \times \frac{\sqrt{5}}{5} - \frac{2}{3} \times \frac{2\sqrt{5}}{5}$$
$$= \frac{5}{15} - \frac{4\sqrt{5}}{15}$$
$$= \mathbf{\frac{5-4\sqrt{5}}{15}}$$

2.3.3 The Double Angle Formulae

$$\sin 2A = 2\sin A\cos A$$

$$\cos 2A = \cos^2 A - \sin^2 A$$
$$= 2\cos^2 A - 1$$
$$= 1 - 2\sin^2 A$$

The double angle formulae can be extended to form other similar ones.

$$\sin 4A = 2\sin 2A\cos 2A \qquad \cos 4A = \cos^2 2A - \sin^2 2A$$
$$\sin 6A = 2\sin 3A\cos 3A \qquad \cos 6A = \cos^2 3A - \sin^2 3A$$

You can also form formulae involving fractional terms.

$$\sin A = 2\sin\tfrac{A}{2}\cos\tfrac{A}{2} \qquad \cos A = \cos^2\tfrac{A}{2} - \sin^2\tfrac{A}{2}$$

Example 1: If $\sin\theta = \frac{1}{5}$, and $0 < \theta < \frac{\pi}{2}$, find the exact value of $\cos 2\theta$ and $\sin 2\theta$.

$\sin\theta = \frac{1}{5}$

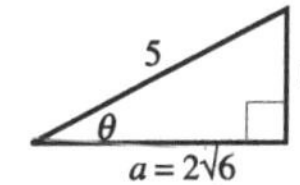

By Pythagoras' Theorem

$$5^2 = a^2 + 1^2$$
$$a^2 = 5^2 - 1^2 = 24$$
$$a = \sqrt{24}$$
$$= 2\sqrt{6}$$

$$\cos\theta = \frac{a}{h} = \frac{2\sqrt{6}}{5}$$

$$\cos 2\theta = \cos^2\theta - \sin^2\theta$$
$$= \left(\frac{2\sqrt{6}}{5}\right)^2 - \left(\frac{1}{5}\right)^2$$
$$= \frac{24}{25} - \frac{1}{25}$$
$$= \mathbf{\frac{23}{25}}$$

$$\sin 2\theta = 2\sin\theta\cos\theta$$
$$= 2 \times \frac{1}{5} \times \frac{2\sqrt{6}}{5}$$
$$= \mathbf{\frac{4\sqrt{6}}{25}}$$

Example 2: By writing $\cos 3x$ as $\cos(2x + x)$, show that $\cos 3x = 4\cos^3 x - 3\cos x$.

$$\cos 3x = \cos(2x + x)$$
$$= \cos 2x\cos x - \sin 2x\sin x$$
$$= (2\cos^2 x - 1)\cos x - 2\sin x\cos x\sin x$$
$$= 2\cos^3 x - \cos x - 2\sin^2 x\cos x$$
$$= 2\cos^3 x - \cos x - 2(1 - \cos^2 x)\cos x$$
$$= 2\cos^3 x - \cos x - 2\cos x + 2\cos^3 x$$
$$= \mathbf{4\cos^3 x - 3\cos x}$$

2.3.4 The Triangle Rules

In Standard Grade, you met the following rules for use with non-right angled triangles. Remember to use "the sum of angles in a triangle = 180°" to find extra information if required.

For any triangle ABC:

The Sine Rule

$$\frac{a}{\sin A} = \frac{b}{\sin B} = \frac{c}{\sin C}$$

The Cosine Rule

$$a^2 = b^2 + c^2 - 2bc\cos A$$

$$\cos A = \frac{b^2 + c^2 - a^2}{2bc}$$

The Area of a Triangle

$$Area = \frac{1}{2}ab\sin C$$

In Standard Grade, the examples were normally numerical. In Higher, they will often be algebraic and involve the addition or double angle formulae.

Example 1: ABC is an isosceles triangle with sizes as shown.
Show that $a = 2b\cos\theta°$.

A
b
θ°
B
a
C

$B = \theta°$ $C = \theta°$

$A = (180 - 2\theta)°$ ***3rd angle in triangle.***

Use $\sin(180 - 2\theta)° = \sin 2\theta°$*, or use the addition formula to expand* $\sin(180 - 2\theta)°$*.*

$$\sin(180-2\theta)° = \sin 180°\cos 2\theta° - \cos 180°\sin 2\theta°$$
$$= 0 \times \cos 2\theta° - (-1) \times \sin 2\theta°$$
$$= \sin 2\theta°$$

By the Sine Rule

$$\frac{a}{\sin A} = \frac{b}{\sin B} = \frac{c}{\sin C}$$

$$\frac{a}{\sin(180-2\theta)°} = \frac{b}{\sin\theta°}$$

$$\frac{a}{\sin 2\theta°} = \frac{b}{\sin\theta°}$$

$$a = \frac{b\sin 2\theta°}{\sin\theta°}$$

$$a = \frac{b \times 2\sin\theta°\cos\theta°}{\sin\theta°}$$

$$\boldsymbol{a = 2b\cos\theta°}$$

Example 2: The diagram shows a regular pyramid with a square base of sidelength 3 cm and slant edges of length 6 cm. Angle AEB is θ.

Show that the exact value of $\cos\theta$ is $\frac{7}{8}$ and find the exact value of $\sin\theta$.

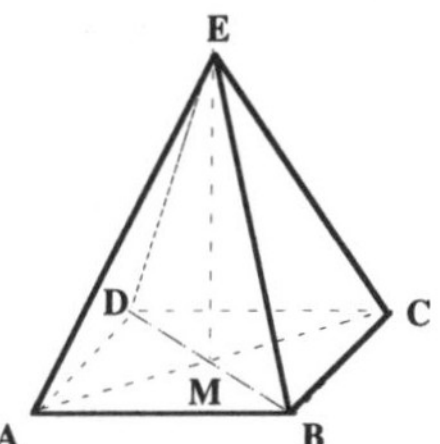

Use the Cosine Rule in triangle AEB to find $\cos\theta$.

By the Cosine rule in ΔEAB

$$\cos E = \frac{a^2 + b^2 - e^2}{2ab}$$

$$\cos\theta = \frac{6^2 + 6^2 - 3^2}{2\times6\times6}$$

$$= \frac{63}{72}$$

$$= \frac{7}{8}$$

Now use the method from Section 2.3.1 for finding the exact value of sin θ given the exact value of cos θ.

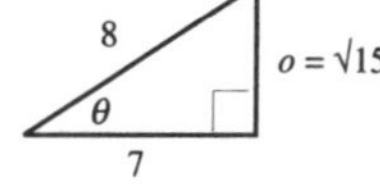

$o = \sqrt{15}$

By Pythagoras' Theorem

$$8^2 = o^2 + 7^2$$

$$o^2 = 8^2 - 7^2$$

$$= 15$$

$$o = \sqrt{15}$$

$$\sin\theta = \frac{o}{h}$$

$$= \frac{\sqrt{15}}{8}$$

2.3.5 Three Dimensional Trigonometry

P is a point. Q is a point in a plane such that the line PQ makes a right angle with the plane in any direction.

Q is called the **perpendicular projection of P in the plane.**

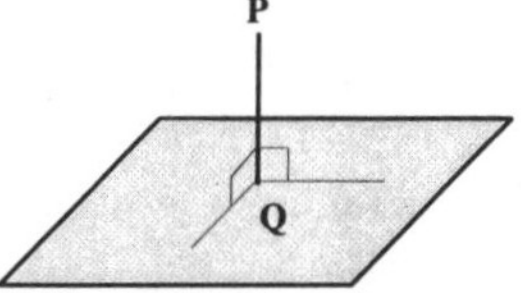

PR meets the plane at R.

You define **the angle between the line and the plane** to be the angle PRQ, where Q is the perpendicular projection of P in the plane.

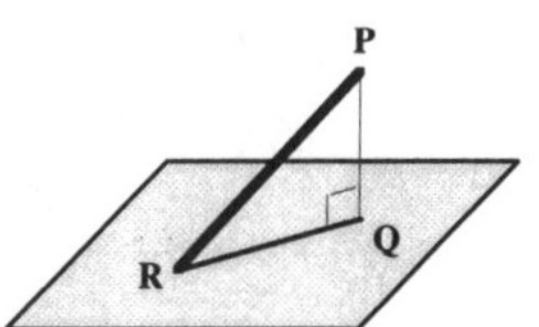

Two planes will always meet in a straight line.

The planes shown meet in the line XY.
P is any point on the line XY.

R is a point in one plane such that PR is perpendicular to XY. Q is a point in the other plane such that PQ is perpendicular to XY.

You define **the angle between the two planes** to be the angle QPR.

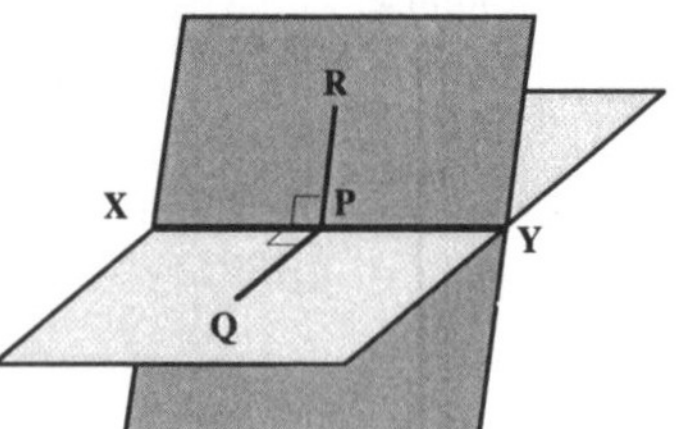

To find the angle between a line and a plane, or the angle between two planes in a 3-dimensional trig problem:

1. Identify the required angle and find a triangle containing the angle.
   A sketch of the situation may help you.

2. Find a triangle (right angled if possible) which contains this angle.
   Draw it separately and find as many lengths as you can.
   You may have to use other triangles to do this.

3. Use trig to find the required angle - simple trig for a right angled triangle or the trig rules from Section 2.3.4 for a non-right angled triangle.

Example: ABCDE is a pyramid such that E is equidistant from A, B, C and D. The pyramid has height 8 cm and a square base of side 6 cm.
(a) Find the angle AE makes with the base.
(b) Find the angle face EBC makes with the base.

(a)

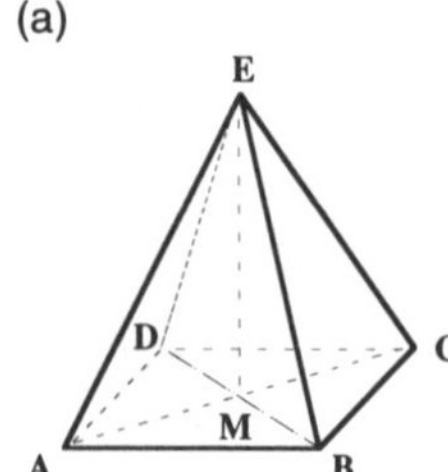

The diagonals of the base intersect at M. M is the perpendicular projection of E in the base.

The angle between edge AE and the base is EAM.

Find AM by first finding AC.

By Pythagoras' Theorem in the right angled triangle ACB

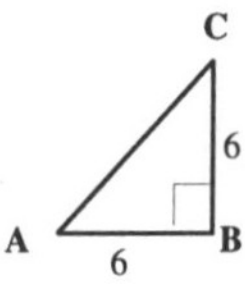

$$AC^2 = AB^2 + BC^2$$
$$AC^2 = 6^2 + 6^2$$
$$= 72$$
$$AC = \sqrt{72}$$
$$= 8.48...$$
$$AM = \frac{8.48...}{2} = 4.24...$$

Sketch triangle EAM.

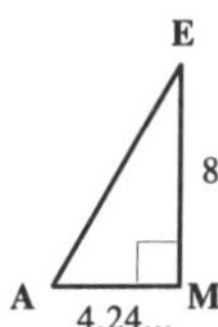

$$\tan A = \frac{8}{4.24...} = 1.885...$$
$$A = 62.06...$$

The angle between AE and the base is **62.1°** to 1dp.

(b)

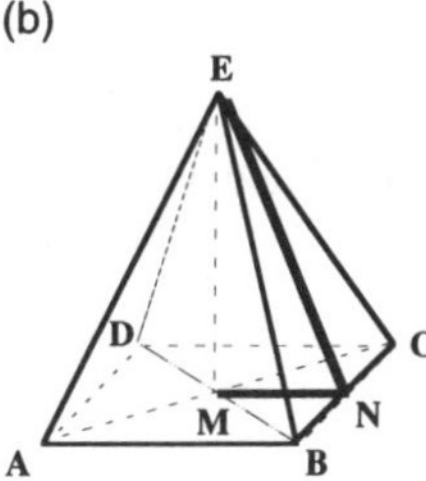

N is the midpoint of BC.

The angle between face EBC and the base is ENM.

Sketch triangle EMN.

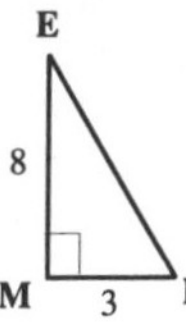

$$\tan N = \frac{8}{3} = 2.66...$$
$$N = 69.44...$$

The angle between face EBC and the base is **69.4°** to 1dp.

2.3.6 Solving Trig Equations

The methods of solving trig equations were covered in Standard Grade and have been summarised here.

You can make use of the three diagrams used in the Standard Grade Revision Book.

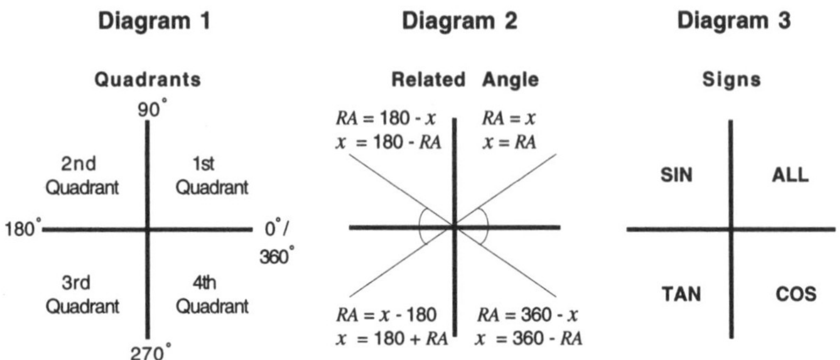

1. Use Diagram 3 to decide which quadrants the solutions, x, will be in. There will be two quadrants in which each ratio is either positive or negative.

2. Find the **related angle (RA)**. Ignore any negative sign and find the angle between 0° and 90° which gives that ratio value. You can use the calculator for this unless it is an exact value.

3. Use Diagram 2 to decide what the solutions (x values) are. Remember, the related angle is always added to or subtracted from 0° / 180° / 360°, never 90° or 270°. Notice that in the 1st Quadrant, the related angle is the solution itself.

The same method is used when the trig function uses radians, but solutions should then be given in radians. You can tell which units are being used by the nature of the domain values. The degree sign will always be used when working in degrees.

Exact values should be used where possible.

Example 1: Solve $\sin x^\circ = -0.5$ for $0 \le x < 360$.

sine is negative in 3rd and 4th Quadrants

$$\begin{aligned} RA &= \sin^{-1} 0.5 \text{ (Note: ignore the "}-\text{" sign.)} \\ &= 30^\circ \end{aligned}$$

3rd Quadrant : $x = 180 + RA$

$= 180 + 30 = 210$

4th Quadrant : $x = 360 - RA$

$= 360 - 30 = 330$

Solution: $x = \mathbf{210}$ or $x = \mathbf{330}$

Example 2: Solve $\sqrt{2}\cos x - 1 = 0$ for $0 \le x < 2\pi$.

$$\sqrt{2}\cos x - 1 = 0$$

$$\cos x = \frac{1}{\sqrt{2}}$$

cosine is positive in 1st and 4th Quadrants

$$RA = \cos^{-1}\tfrac{1}{\sqrt{2}}$$

$$= \tfrac{\pi}{4}$$

1st Quadrant : $x = RA$

$= \tfrac{\pi}{4}$

4th Quadrant : $x = 2\pi - RA$

$= 2\pi - \tfrac{\pi}{4} = \tfrac{7\pi}{4}$

Solution: $x = \boldsymbol{\tfrac{\pi}{4}}$ or $x = \boldsymbol{\tfrac{7\pi}{4}}$

Example 3: Solve $3\tan^2 x - 1 = 0$ for $0 \le x < 2\pi$.

$$3\tan^2 x - 1 = 0$$

$$\tan^2 x = \tfrac{1}{3}$$

$$\tan x = \pm\tfrac{1}{\sqrt{3}}$$

± means consider all four Quadrants

$$RA = \tan^{-1}\tfrac{1}{\sqrt{3}}$$

$$= \tfrac{\pi}{6}$$

1st Quadrant : $x = RA$

$= \tfrac{\pi}{6}$

2nd Quadrant : $x = \pi - RA$

$= \pi - \tfrac{\pi}{6} = \tfrac{5\pi}{6}$

3rd Quadrant : $x = \pi + RA$

$= \pi + \tfrac{\pi}{6} = \tfrac{7\pi}{6}$

3rd Quadrant : $x = 2\pi - RA$

$= 2\pi - \tfrac{\pi}{6} = \tfrac{11\pi}{6}$

Solution: $x = \boldsymbol{\tfrac{\pi}{6}}$ or $x = \boldsymbol{\tfrac{5\pi}{6}}$ or $x = \boldsymbol{\tfrac{7\pi}{6}}$ or $x = \boldsymbol{\tfrac{11\pi}{6}}$

Some examples will require more algebraic manipulation before applying the trig equation procedures. In the following example, you must first factorise the equation as a quadratic in $\cos x$.

Example 4: Solve $\cos^2 x - 4\cos x + 3 = 0$ for $0 \le x < 2\pi$.

$$\cos^2 x - 4\cos x + 3 = 0$$
$$(\cos x - 3)(\cos x - 1) = 0$$

$\cos x - 3 = 0$ or $\cos x - 1 = 0$

$\cos x = 3$ $\cos x = 1$ ⟵ *You can obtain the x values in cases like this* ***(cos x = 1, −1 or 0)*** *from your knowledge of the shape of the cosine graph. Similarly for sine.*

no solutions $x = 0$

Solution: $x = \mathbf{0}$

2.3.7 Solving Trig Equations (Compound Angles)

Functions like $\sin(ax + b)$ are periodic with period $\frac{360}{a}$ in degrees or $\frac{2\pi}{a}$ in radians.

For an equation involving a function with period P, if x is a solution,
then $x \pm$ P, $x \pm$2P, $x \pm$ 3P, ... will also be solutions,

eg if $x = 30$ is a solution and the period is 120°, then further solutions will be:

$x = 30 + 120 = 150$, $x = 30 - 120 = -90$,
$x = 30 + 240 = 270$, $x = 30 - 240 = -210$,
etc.

You must find all the solutions within the specified domain.

Example 1: Solve $\sin 2x = 0.8$ for $0 \le x < 360$.

sine is positive in 1st and 2nd Quadrants, period is 180°

$$RA = \sin^{-1} 0.8$$
$$= 53.13...^\circ$$

1st Quadrant: $2x = RA$
$= 53.13...$
$x = \frac{53.13...}{2} = 26.56... = 26.6$ to 1dp

2nd Quadrant: $2x = 180 - RA$
$= 180 - 53.13... = 126.86...$
$x = \frac{126.86...}{2} = 63.43... = 63.4$ to 1dp

Basic solutions $x = 26.6$ or $x = 63.4$
Add 180° $x = 206.6$ or $x = 243.4$
Add 360° out of specified domain

Solution: $x = \mathbf{26.6}$ or $x = \mathbf{63.4}$ or $x = \mathbf{206.6}$ or $x = \mathbf{243.4}$

Example 2: Solve $2\cos(3x - \frac{\pi}{3}) + 1 = 0$ for $0 \le x \le \pi$.

$2\cos(3x - \frac{\pi}{3}) + 1 = 0$
$\cos(3x - \frac{\pi}{3}) = -\frac{1}{2}$

cosine is negative in 2nd and 3rd Quadrants, period is $\frac{2\pi}{3}$

$RA = \cos^{-1}\frac{1}{2}$
$= \frac{\pi}{3}$

2nd Quadrant: $3x - \frac{\pi}{3} = \pi - RA$
$= \pi - \frac{\pi}{3} = \frac{2\pi}{3}$
$3x = \frac{2\pi}{3} + \frac{\pi}{3} = \pi$
$x = \frac{\pi}{3}$

3rd Quadrant: $3x - \frac{\pi}{3} = \pi + RA$
$= \pi + \frac{\pi}{3} = \frac{4\pi}{3}$
$3x = \frac{4\pi}{3} + \frac{\pi}{3} = \frac{5\pi}{3}$
$x = \frac{5\pi}{9}$

Basic solutions $x = \frac{\pi}{3}$ or $x = \frac{5\pi}{9}$
Add $\frac{2\pi}{3}$ $x = \frac{\pi}{3} + \frac{2\pi}{3} = \pi$ or $x = \frac{5\pi}{9} + \frac{2\pi}{3} = \frac{11\pi}{9}$
(out of specified domain)

Solution: $x = \boldsymbol{\frac{\pi}{3}}$ or $x = \boldsymbol{\frac{5\pi}{9}}$ or $x = \boldsymbol{\pi}$

2.3.8 Solving Trig Equations using the Sine Double Angle Formula

For an equation of the form

$$a\sin 2x + b\sin x = 0 \qquad \text{or} \qquad a\sin 2x + b\cos x = 0$$

you can use the double angle formula for $\sin 2x$ to give an equation which can be factorised using a common factor. You can then solve the resulting simple equations as in Section 2.3.6.

Example: Solve algebraically the equation $\sqrt{2}\sin 2x - 2\sin x = 0$ where $0 \leq x < 2\pi$.

$$\sqrt{2}\sin 2x - 2\sin x = 0$$

$$\sqrt{2} \times 2\sin x\cos x - 2\sin x = 0$$

$$2\sin x(\sqrt{2}\cos x - 1) = 0$$

$2\sin x = 0$ or $\sqrt{2}\cos x - 1 = 0$

$\sin x = 0$ $\qquad$ $\cos x = \frac{1}{\sqrt{2}}$

$x = 0, \ \pi$ $\qquad$ $RA = \cos^{-1}\frac{1}{\sqrt{2}} = \frac{\pi}{4}$

cosine is positive in 1st and 4th Quadrants

1st Quadrant: $x = \frac{\pi}{4}$

4th Quadrant: $x = 2\pi - \frac{\pi}{4} = \frac{7\pi}{4}$

Solution: $\boldsymbol{x = 0}$ or $\boldsymbol{x = \frac{\pi}{4}}$ or $\boldsymbol{x = \pi}$ or $\boldsymbol{x = \frac{7\pi}{4}}$

2.3.9 Solving Trig Equations using the Cosine Double Angle Formula

For an equation of the form

$$a\cos 2x + b\sin x + c = 0 \qquad \text{or} \qquad a\cos 2x + b\cos x + c = 0$$

you can use a double angle formula for $\cos 2x$ to give a quadratic equation in either $\cos x$ or $\sin x$ which can be factorised into two brackets.

If there is a $\cos x$ term in the equation, use $\boldsymbol{\cos 2x = 2\cos^2 x - 1}$ to get a quadratic in $\cos x$.

If there is a $\sin x$ term in the equation, use $\boldsymbol{\cos 2x = 1 - 2\sin^2 x}$ to get a quadratic in $\sin x$.

Example 1: Solve algebraically the equation $\cos 2x^\circ + \cos x^\circ = 0$ where $0 \le x < 360$.

$$\cos 2x^\circ + \cos x^\circ = 0$$
$$\left(2\cos^2 x^\circ - 1\right) + \cos x^\circ = 0$$
$$2\cos^2 x^\circ + \cos x^\circ - 1 = 0$$
$$(2\cos x^\circ - 1)(\cos x^\circ + 1) = 0$$

$2\cos x^\circ - 1 = 0$ or $\cos x^\circ + 1 = 0$

$\cos x^\circ = \frac{1}{2}$ $\qquad$ $\cos x^\circ = -1$

$RA = \cos^{-1}\frac{1}{2} = 60^\circ$ $\qquad$ From the $\cos$ graph

cosine is positive in 1st and 4th Quadrants $\qquad$ $x = 180$

1st Quadrant: $x = 60$

4th Quadrant: $x = 360 - 60 = 300$

Solution: $x = \mathbf{60}$ or $x = \mathbf{180}$ or $x = \mathbf{300}$

Example 2: Solve algebraically the equation $\cos 2x + 3\sin x + 1 = 0$ where $0 \le x < 2\pi$.

$$\cos 2x + 3\sin x + 1 = 0$$
$$\left(1 - 2\sin^2 x\right) + 3\sin x + 1 = 0$$
$$-2\sin^2 x + 3\sin x + 2 = 0$$
$$2\sin^2 x - 3\sin x - 2 = 0$$
$$(2\sin x + 1)(\sin x - 2) = 0$$

$2\sin x + 1 = 0$ or $\sin x - 2 = 0$

$\sin x = -\frac{1}{2}$ $\qquad$ $\sin x = 2$

$RA = \sin^{-1}\frac{1}{2} = \frac{\pi}{6}$ $\qquad$ No solutions

sine is negative in 3rd and 4th Quadrants

3rd Quadrant: $x = \pi + \frac{\pi}{6} = \frac{7\pi}{6}$

4th Quadrant: $x = 2\pi - \frac{\pi}{6} = \frac{11\pi}{6}$

Solution: $x = \mathbf{\frac{7\pi}{6}}$ or $x = \mathbf{\frac{11\pi}{6}}$

2.4 CIRCLES

2.4.1 The Equation of a Circle

The equation of a circle, centre (a,b) and radius r is:

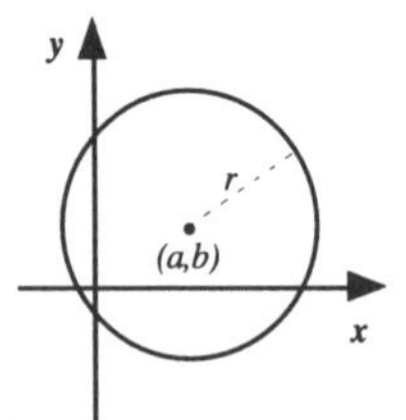

$$(x - a)^2 + (y - b)^2 = r^2$$

For a circle with its centre at the origin (0,0), this becomes:

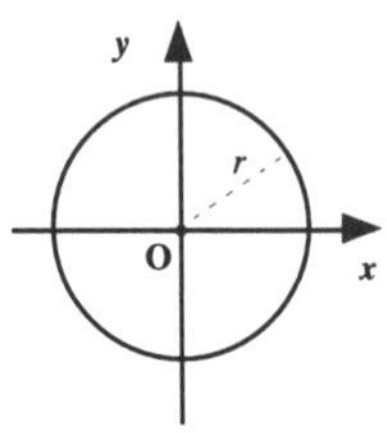

$$x^2 + y^2 = r^2$$

These forms of the circle equation are the easiest to work with as you can quickly obtain the centre and radius from them. Unless a question demands otherwise, you should leave the equation in one of these forms.

Example: The circle with centre A has an equation

$$(x + 1)^2 + (y - 3)^2 = 4.$$

The circle with centre B has a radius double that of the circle with centre A. The line of centres is parallel to the x-axis. Find the equation of the circle with centre B.

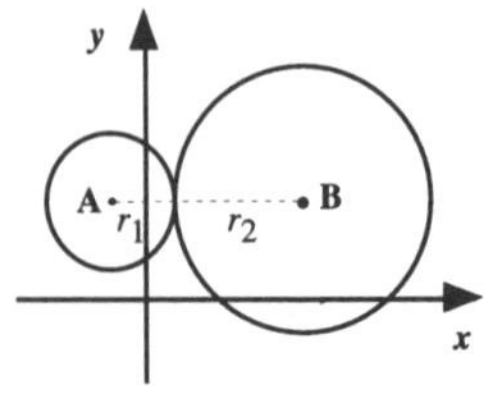

Circle centre A:

$$A = (-1,3) \qquad r_1 = \sqrt{4} = 2$$

Circle centre B:

$$r_2 = 2 \times 2 = 4 \qquad B = (-1 + 2 + 4, 3) = (5,3)$$

Equation:

$$\mathbf{(x - 5)^2 + (y - 3)^2 = 16}$$

2.4.2 The General Form of the Equation of a Circle

By multiplying out the brackets in the above form, you can show that every circle will have an equation containing x^2, y^2 and constant terms. It may also contain x and y terms.

$$x^2 + y^2 + 2gx + 2fy + c = 0$$

is the general form of the equation of the circle

centre $(-g, -f)$ and radius $\sqrt{g^2 + f^2 - c}$.

Every equation of the form $x^2 + y^2 + 2gx + 2fy + c = 0$ will represent a circle provided:

$$g^2 + f^2 - c > 0$$

You must know this condition, and be able to use it to decide if a given equation represents a circle or not.

Example 1: Decide whether each of the following equations represents a circle or not. If it does, state the centre and radius of the circle.

(a) $x^2 + y^2 + 6x - 5y + 18 = 0$

(b) $3x^2 + 3y^2 - 18x + 12y - 9 = 0$

(a) $x^2 + y^2 + 6x - 5y + 18 = 0$

$x^2 + y^2 + 2gx + 2fy + c = 0$

$2g = 6 \qquad 2f = -5 \qquad c = 18$

$g = 3 \qquad f = -2.5$

First check the condition.

$g^2 + f^2 - c = 3^2 + (-2.5)^2 - 18$

$= -2.75 < 0$

This does **not** represent a circle.

(b) $3x^2 + 3y^2 - 18x + 12y - 9 = 0$

$x^2 + y^2 - 6x + 4y - 3 = 0$

$x^2 + y^2 + 2gx + 2fy + c = 0$

$2g = -6 \qquad 2f = 4 \qquad c = -3$

$g = -3 \qquad f = 2$

$g^2 + f^2 - c = (-3)^2 + 2^2 - (-3) = 16$

$r = \sqrt{g^2 + f^2 - c} = \sqrt{16} = 4$

$(-g, -f) = (-(-3), -2)) = (3, -2)$

This **does** represent a circle, with centre **(3, −2)** and radius **4**.

Example 2: The point $(a,-3)$ lies on the circumference of the circle with equation $x^2 + y^2 - 2x - 2y - 23 = 0$. Find the possible values of a.

$$x^2 + y^2 - 2x - 2y - 23 = 0 \qquad (a,-3)$$

Substitute the coordinates into the circle equation.

$$a^2 + (-3)^2 - 2a - 2\times(-3) - 23 = 0$$
$$a^2 - 2a - 8 = 0$$
$$(a-4)(a+2) = 0$$
$$a - 4 = 0 \quad \text{or} \quad a + 2 = 0$$
$$a = \mathbf{4} \qquad a = \mathbf{-2}$$

2.4.3 Tangents to a Circle

In Standard Grade you learned that a tangent meets the radius at the point of contact at right angles. By using this you can find the equation of a tangent (see Example 1) or the length of a tangent from a point (see Example 2).

Example 1: Find the equation of the tangent to the circle with equation $x^2 + y^2 - 6x - 4y - 12 = 0$ at the point $(6,6)$.

$$x^2 + y^2 - 6x - 4y - 12 = 0$$
$$x^2 + y^2 + 2gx + 2fy + c = 0$$
$$2g = -6 \qquad 2f = -4 \qquad c = -12$$
$$g = -3 \qquad f = -2$$
$$(-g,-f) = (-(-3),-(-2)) = (3,2)$$

$$m_{radius} = \frac{y_2 - y_1}{x_2 - x_1} = \frac{6-2}{6-3} = \frac{4}{3}$$

$$m_1 m_2 = -1$$
$$\tfrac{4}{3} \times m_2 = -1$$
$$m_2 = -\tfrac{3}{4}$$

✔ $m = -\frac{3}{4}$ ✔ $(a,b) = (6,6)$

$$y - b = m(x - a)$$
$$y - 6 = -\tfrac{3}{4}(x - 6)$$
$$4y - 24 = -3x + 18$$
$$\mathbf{3x + 4y = 42}$$

Example 2: Find the length of the tangent to the circle with equation $x^2 + y^2 + 4x + 4y - 17 = 0$ from the point P $(9,-4)$.

Use T to represent the point of contact.
Note that you do not actually need to find the coordinates of T.

$$x^2 + y^2 + 4x + 4y - 17 = 0$$
$$x^2 + y^2 + 2gx + 2fy + c = 0$$
$$2g = 4 \qquad 2f = 4 \qquad c = -17$$
$$g = 2 \qquad f = 2$$
$$(-g, -f) = (-2, -2)$$

$$\text{radius} = \sqrt{g^2 + f^2 - c}$$
$$= \sqrt{2^2 + 2^2 - (-17)}$$
$$= \sqrt{25} = 5$$

$$CP = \sqrt{(x_2 - x_1)^2 + (y_2 - y_1)^2}$$
$$= \sqrt{(9 - (-2))^2 + (-4 - (-2))^2}$$
$$= \sqrt{125}$$

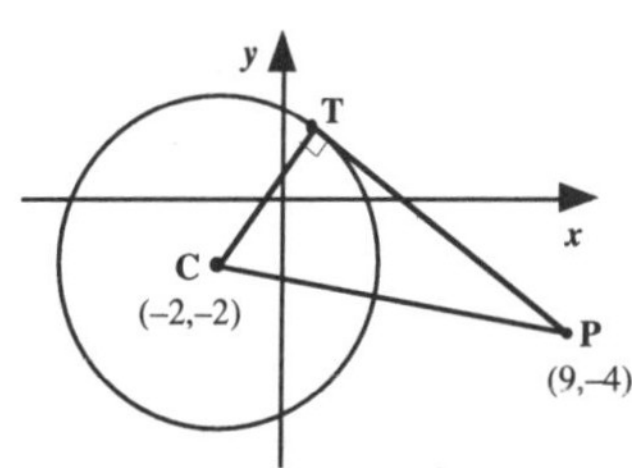

By Pythagoras' Theorem

$$CP^2 = CT^2 + TP^2$$
$$125 = 5^2 + TP^2$$
$$TP^2 = 100$$
$$TP = \sqrt{100} = 10$$

The tangent from P has length **10**.

2.4.4 The Intersection of a Line and a Circle

When a straight line meets a circle, it will intersect it in either two points, in one point if it is a **tangent**, or it will not intersect it at all.

Since an **intersection equation**, which will be quadratic, can be formed from the equations of the line and the circle, you can use the discriminant of the intersection equation to determine how the line cuts the circle, as in Section 2.1.12 with curves.

2 intersection points $b^2 - 4ac > 0$	**1 intersection point** $b^2 - 4ac = 0$	**no intersection points** $b^2 - 4ac < 0$

The methods are similar to those used with parabolas.

1. Set up the intersection equation by substituting the straight line equation into the circle equation.

2. Use the discriminant to find the nature of the intersection points.

3. If you require to find the actual intersection points, solve the intersection equation to find the x-coordinates and substitute these into the straight line equation to find the y-coordinates.

Sometimes it may be easier to substitute for x first (see Example 3).

Example 1: Show that the line with equation $y = 3x + 3$ meets the circle with equation $x^2 + y^2 - 2x - 2y - 23 = 0$, in two points.

$x^2 + y^2 - 2x - 2y - 23 = 0 \qquad y = 3x + 3$

Intersection Equation:

$$x^2 + (3x+3)^2 - 2x - 2(3x+3) - 23 = 0$$
$$x^2 + 9x^2 + 18x + 9 - 2x - 6x - 6 - 23 = 0$$
$$10x^2 + 10x - 20 = 0$$
$$a = 10 \qquad b = 10 \qquad c = -20$$

$$disc = b^2 - 4ac$$
$$= 10^2 - 4 \times 10 \times (-20)$$
$$= 900$$
$$> 0$$

The line meets the circle in **two distinct points.**

Example 2: Show that the line with equation $y = 2x - 10$ is a tangent to the circle with equation $x^2 + y^2 - 4x + 2y = 0$, and find the point of contact.

$x^2 + y^2 - 4x + 2y = 0 \qquad y = 2x - 10$

Intersection Equation:

$$x^2 + (2x-10)^2 - 4x + 2(2x-10) = 0$$
$$x^2 + 4x^2 - 40x + 100 - 4x + 4x - 20 = 0$$
$$5x^2 - 40x + 80 = 0$$
$$5(x^2 - 8x + 16) = 0$$
$$5(x-4)^2 = 0$$
$$x - 4 = 0$$
$$x = 4$$

You could use the discriminant at this point to show it is a tangent.

However since you need to find the point of contact in any case, you can just continue to solve the intersection equation.

Since the intersection equation has equal roots, **the line is a tangent.**

$x = 4 \qquad y = 2x - 10$

$\qquad\qquad = 2 \times 4 - 10$

$\qquad\qquad = -2$ The point of contact is **(4,–2)**.

Example 3: The line with equation $x - 3y = k$ is a tangent to the circle with equation $x^2 + y^2 - 6x + 8y + 15 = 0$. Find the possible values of k.

$x^2 + y^2 - 6x + 8y + 15 = 0 \qquad x - 3y = k$

$x = 3y + k$

It is easier here to find x in terms of y. Otherwise you would need to work with fractions.

Intersection Equation:

$$(3y+k)^2 + y^2 - 6(3y+k) + 8y + 15 = 0$$
$$9y^2 + 6ky + k^2 + y^2 - 18y - 6k + 8y + 15 = 0$$
$$10y^2 + (6k-10)y + \left(k^2 - 6k + 15\right) = 0$$

$a = 10 \qquad b = 6k - 10 \qquad c = k^2 - 6k + 15$

For tangency $\qquad b^2 - 4ac = 0$

$$(6k-10)^2 - 4 \times 10(k^2 - 6k + 15) = 0$$
$$36k^2 - 120k + 100 - 40k^2 + 240k - 600 = 0$$
$$-4k^2 + 120k - 500 = 0$$
$$-4(k^2 - 30k + 125) = 0$$
$$-4(k-5)(k-25) = 0$$

$k - 5 = 0$ or $k - 25 = 0$

$\mathbf{k = 5} \qquad \mathbf{k = 25}$

2.4.5 Touching Circles

When two circles meet in a single point, you say they are **touching**. In this case the tangent at the touching point will be a **common tangent**, a tangent to both circles.

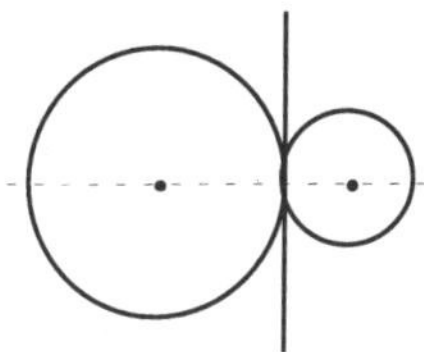

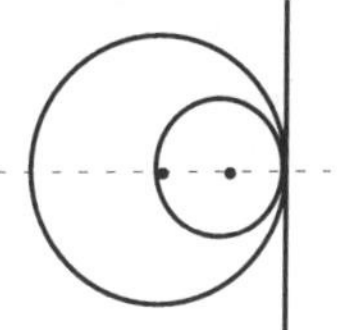

The **line of centres**, the line through the centres of the two circles, will pass through the touching point and make a right angle with the common tangent.

To show that two circles touch, you can show that the tangent to one circle is also a tangent to the other at the same point. You could also show that the centres and the touching point are collinear and compare the distance between the centres and the length of the radii.

Example: Two congruent circles, with centres A $(-1,-1)$ and B $(7,5)$, touch at a point. Find the equation of the common tangent.

The touching point will be the midpoint of AB. The tangent will be perpendicular to AB.

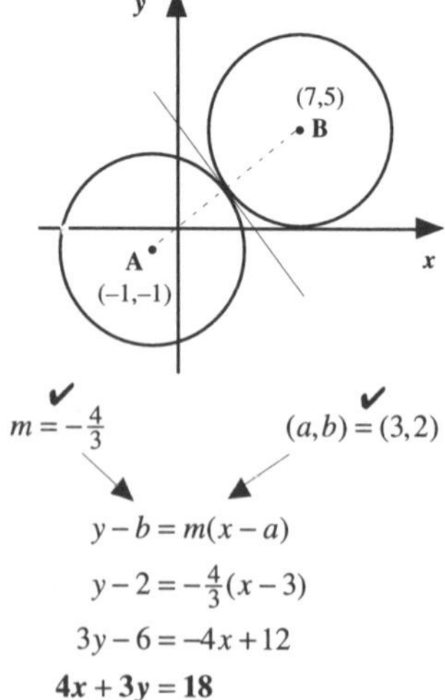

$$M_{AB} = \left(\frac{x_1 + x_2}{2}, \frac{y_1 + y_2}{2}\right)$$
$$= \left(\frac{-1+7}{2}, \frac{-1+5}{2}\right)$$
$$= (3,2)$$

$$m_{AB} = \frac{y_2 - y_1}{x_2 - x_1}$$
$$= \frac{5-(-1)}{7-(-1)}$$
$$= \tfrac{6}{8} = \tfrac{3}{4}$$

$$m_1 m_2 = -1$$
$$\tfrac{3}{4} \times m_2 = -1$$
$$m_2 = -\tfrac{4}{3}$$

✔ $m = -\tfrac{4}{3}$ ✔ $(a,b) = (3,2)$

$$y - b = m(x - a)$$
$$y - 2 = -\tfrac{4}{3}(x - 3)$$
$$3y - 6 = -4x + 12$$
$$\mathbf{4x + 3y = 18}$$

2.4.6 Finding the Equation of a Circle Through Three Points

If you know three points on the circumference of a circle, its equation can be found using three simultaneous equations in three unknowns. The coordinates of each point are substituted into the general equation of the circle to set up three equations in g, f and c.

This method is no longer required for Higher, so there will not be a question in the exam which requires this approach. You may find, however, the points lead to two simultaneous equations in two unknowns.

In Standard Grade, you learned that if three points on the circumference of a circle form a right angled triangle, then the hypotenuse is the diameter of the circle. This would allow you to find the equation of the circle in this particular case.

If an example of this type came up in the exam, either the coordinates will obviously make a right angled triangle (as in the example below), or the question will ask you to show it is a right angled triangle first.

You could use gradients or the Converse of Pythagoras' Theorem to do this.

Example: Find the equation of the circle passing through the points (5,4), (–3,–2) and (5,–2).

Name the points to make it easier to follow what you are doing.

The three points form a right angled triangle with a right angle at C (5,–2).

The line joining B (–3,–2) to A (5,4) is a diameter of the circle.

The centre of the circle is at M, the midpoint of AB.

$$\begin{aligned} M_{AB} &= \left(\frac{x_1+x_2}{2}, \frac{y_1+y_2}{2}\right) \\ &= \left(\frac{5+(-3)}{2}, \frac{4+(-2)}{2}\right) \\ &= (1,1) \end{aligned}$$

$$\begin{aligned} \text{radius} &= d_{MA} \\ &= \sqrt{(x_2-x_1)^2+(y_2-y_1)^2} \\ &= \sqrt{(5-1)^2+(4-1)^2} \\ &= \sqrt{25} \\ &= 5 \end{aligned}$$

The circle has equation $(x-1)^2+(y-1)^2=25$.

3.1 VECTORS

3.1.1 Notation and Terminology

A **vector** is defined to be a quantity which has both a size, or **magnitude**, and a **direction** associated with it. It can be helpful to think of a vector as a movement.

A vector can be represented pictorially using a **directed line segment**. This is shown by a line with an arrow.

The length of the line indicates the magnitude of the vector, and the arrow indicates the direction. It is particularly effective on squared paper.

A vector is often named using a letter in bold type, eg $\boldsymbol{u}$.

It can also be named by using the letters of its endpoints. In this case, an arrow is shown above the letters indicating the direction from A to B, eg $\overrightarrow{\mathrm{AB}}$.

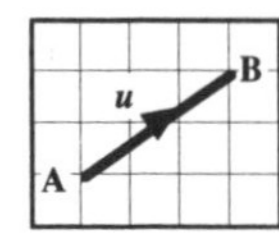

Any directed line segment with the same magnitude and direction will represent the same vector.

In the parallelogram opposite

$$\overrightarrow{\mathrm{AB}} = \overrightarrow{\mathrm{DC}} = \boldsymbol{u}, \ \overrightarrow{\mathrm{AD}} = \overrightarrow{\mathrm{BC}} = \boldsymbol{v}.$$

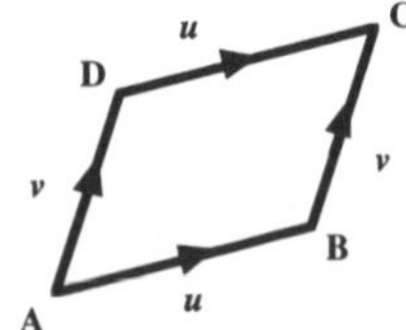

3.1.2 The Component Form of a Vector

Although directed lines give a good visual illustration of vectors, particularly in 2 dimensions, in practice you will normally use the **component form** of a vector which gives the same information in numerical form.

Component form allows you to apply the powerful methods of algebra to vectors.

The 2-dimensional vector $\boldsymbol{u}$, shown above, goes 3 along in the direction of the x-axis and 2 up in the direction of the y-axis.

You write this as $\boldsymbol{u} = \begin{pmatrix} 3 \\ 2 \end{pmatrix}$.

Normally in Higher, vectors will be 3-dimensional, using three components, eg

$$\boldsymbol{u}=\begin{pmatrix}x\\y\\z\end{pmatrix}\qquad \boldsymbol{v}=\begin{pmatrix}-2\\3\\5\end{pmatrix}\qquad \boldsymbol{w}=\begin{pmatrix}0\\0\\-2\end{pmatrix}\qquad \boldsymbol{a}=\begin{pmatrix}-\frac{1}{2}\\1\\\frac{3}{4}\end{pmatrix}$$

In 3 dimensions, the third component is in the direction of the z-axis.

3.1.3 The Basic Vector Operations

The operations of addition, negative, subtraction and multiplication by a scalar are defined for vectors. The definitions are given below in terms of components and illustrated using 2-dimensional vectors.

Addition of Vectors

When two vectors, $\boldsymbol{u}$ and $\boldsymbol{v}$, are added, the **resultant** vector, $\boldsymbol{u} + \boldsymbol{v}$, represents the single movement equivalent to the movement given by $\boldsymbol{u}$, followed by the movement given by $\boldsymbol{v}$.

Vectors must be added **"nose-to-tail"**. The next vector starts from where the last finished. It can be helpful to indicate a resultant vector with a double arrow.

The diagram shows that

$$\boldsymbol{u} + \boldsymbol{v} = \boldsymbol{v} + \boldsymbol{u}.$$

This is known as the **parallelogram rule** for addition of vectors.

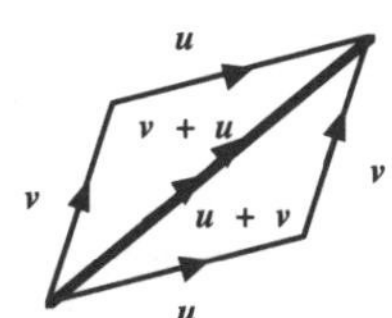

In component form $\boldsymbol{u}=\begin{pmatrix}3\\2\end{pmatrix}$ and $\boldsymbol{v}=\begin{pmatrix}1\\-4\end{pmatrix}$

and $\boldsymbol{u}+\boldsymbol{v}=\begin{pmatrix}3\\2\end{pmatrix}+\begin{pmatrix}1\\-4\end{pmatrix}=\begin{pmatrix}4\\-2\end{pmatrix}.$

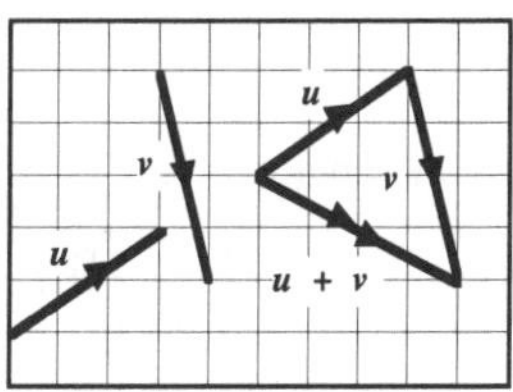

In general:

$$\text{If } u = \begin{pmatrix} x_1 \\ y_1 \\ z_1 \end{pmatrix} \text{ and } v = \begin{pmatrix} x_2 \\ y_2 \\ z_2 \end{pmatrix}, \text{ then } u + v = \begin{pmatrix} x_1 + x_2 \\ y_1 + y_2 \\ z_1 + z_2 \end{pmatrix}.$$

The Negative of a Vector

The negative of vector u is defined to be the vector with the same magnitude but opposite direction, and is written $-u$.

In component form $u = \begin{pmatrix} 3 \\ 2 \end{pmatrix}$ and $-u = -\begin{pmatrix} 3 \\ 2 \end{pmatrix} = \begin{pmatrix} -3 \\ -2 \end{pmatrix}$.

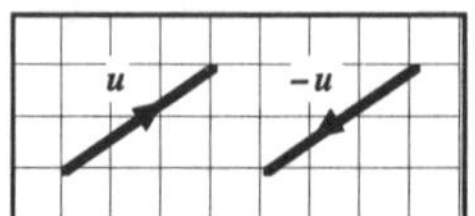

In general:

$$\text{If } u = \begin{pmatrix} x_1 \\ y_1 \\ z_1 \end{pmatrix}, \text{ then } -u = \begin{pmatrix} -x_1 \\ -y_1 \\ -z_1 \end{pmatrix}.$$

Subtraction of Vectors

When two vectors, u and v, are subtracted, the **resultant** vector, $u - v$, is given by adding u and the negative of v. When using components, this can simply be done by subtracting the components of v.

In component form $u = \begin{pmatrix} 3 \\ 2 \end{pmatrix}$ and $v = \begin{pmatrix} 1 \\ -4 \end{pmatrix}$

and $u - v = \begin{pmatrix} 3 \\ 2 \end{pmatrix} - \begin{pmatrix} 1 \\ -4 \end{pmatrix} = \begin{pmatrix} 3-1 \\ 2-(-4) \end{pmatrix} = \begin{pmatrix} 2 \\ 6 \end{pmatrix}$.

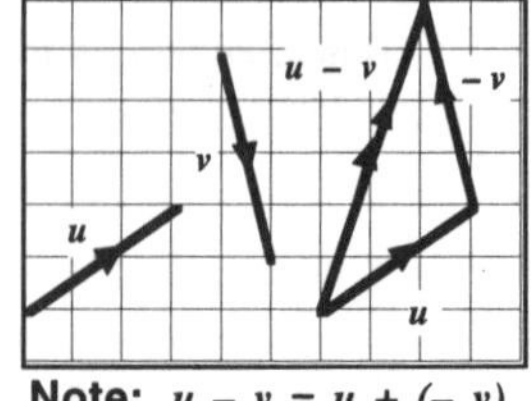

Note: $u - v = u + (-v)$

In general:

$$\text{If } u = \begin{pmatrix} x_1 \\ y_1 \\ z_1 \end{pmatrix} \text{ and } v = \begin{pmatrix} x_2 \\ y_2 \\ z_2 \end{pmatrix}, \text{ then } u - v = \begin{pmatrix} x_1 - x_2 \\ y_1 - y_2 \\ z_1 - z_2 \end{pmatrix}.$$

Multiplication of a Vector by a Scalar

A quantity which is not a vector, ie does not have a direction associated with it, is called a **scalar**. A number is a scalar quantity.

When a vector $\boldsymbol{u}$ is multiplied by a scalar k ($k > 0$), the resultant vector $k\boldsymbol{u}$ will have magnitude k times as big and the same direction as $\boldsymbol{u}$.
If $k < 0$, $k\boldsymbol{u}$ will have the opposite direction.

In component form $\boldsymbol{u} = \begin{pmatrix} 3 \\ 2 \end{pmatrix}$ and

$$2\boldsymbol{u} = 2\begin{pmatrix} 3 \\ 2 \end{pmatrix} = \begin{pmatrix} 2\times3 \\ 2\times2 \end{pmatrix} = \begin{pmatrix} 6 \\ 4 \end{pmatrix}.$$

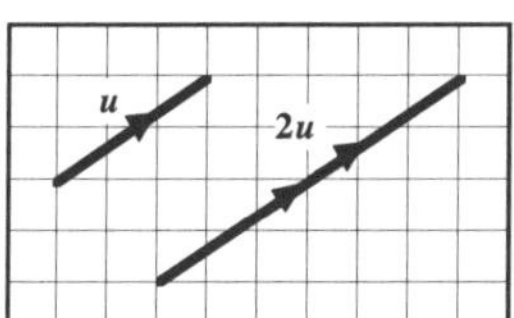

In general:

$$\text{If } \boldsymbol{u} = \begin{pmatrix} x_1 \\ y_1 \\ z_1 \end{pmatrix}, \text{ then } k\boldsymbol{u} = \begin{pmatrix} kx_1 \\ ky_1 \\ kz_1 \end{pmatrix}.$$

The Zero Vector

The vector with no magnitude and no direction is called the **zero vector**.

It is written $\mathbf{0} = \begin{pmatrix} 0 \\ 0 \\ 0 \end{pmatrix}$.

Equal Vectors

Two vectors are equal if their components are equal.

$$\text{If } \boldsymbol{u} = \begin{pmatrix} x_1 \\ y_1 \\ z_1 \end{pmatrix} \text{ and } \boldsymbol{v} = \begin{pmatrix} x_2 \\ y_2 \\ z_2 \end{pmatrix}, \text{ and } \boldsymbol{u} = \boldsymbol{v}, \text{ then } \begin{matrix} x_1 = x_2 \\ y_1 = y_2 \\ z_1 = z_2 \end{matrix}.$$

Example 1: ABCDEFGH is a cuboid, such that $\overrightarrow{AB} = \boldsymbol{u}$, $\overrightarrow{AD} = \boldsymbol{v}$ and $\overrightarrow{AE} = \boldsymbol{w}$.

Express $\overrightarrow{HB}$ in terms of $\boldsymbol{u}$, $\boldsymbol{v}$ and $\boldsymbol{w}$.

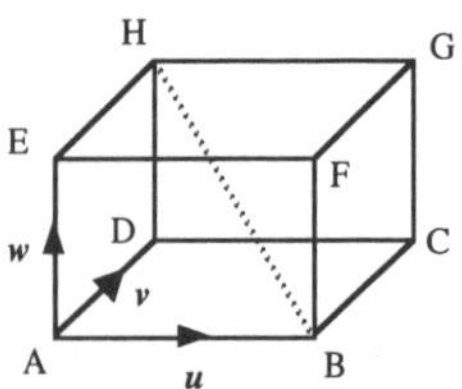

$$\begin{aligned}\overrightarrow{HB} &= \overrightarrow{HE} + \overrightarrow{EA} + \overrightarrow{AB}\\ &= (-\overrightarrow{AD}) + (-\overrightarrow{AE}) + \overrightarrow{AB}\\ &= -\boldsymbol{v} - \boldsymbol{w} + \boldsymbol{u}\\ &= \boldsymbol{u} - \boldsymbol{v} - \boldsymbol{w}\end{aligned}$$

Choose any vector combination that will take you from H to B, then give these vectors in terms of u, v and w (see Section 3.1.1).

Example 2: $\boldsymbol{u} = \begin{pmatrix} a \\ 4 \\ -2 \end{pmatrix}$ and $\boldsymbol{v} = \begin{pmatrix} -3b \\ b \\ -3 \end{pmatrix}$. If $3\boldsymbol{u} - 2\boldsymbol{v} = \boldsymbol{0}$, find a and b.

$$3\boldsymbol{u} - 2\boldsymbol{v} = \boldsymbol{0}$$

$$3\begin{pmatrix} a \\ 4 \\ -2 \end{pmatrix} - 2\begin{pmatrix} -3b \\ b \\ -3 \end{pmatrix} = \begin{pmatrix} 0 \\ 0 \\ 0 \end{pmatrix}$$

$$\begin{pmatrix} 3a+6b \\ 12-2b \\ -6+6 \end{pmatrix} = \begin{pmatrix} 0 \\ 0 \\ 0 \end{pmatrix} \quad \left.\begin{aligned} 3a+6b &= 0 \\ 12-2b &= 0 \end{aligned}\right\}$$

$$\begin{aligned} 12-2b &= 0 \\ 12 &= 2b \\ b &= \mathbf{6} \end{aligned}$$

$$\begin{aligned} 3a+6b &= 0 \\ 3a+6\times 6 &= 0 \\ 3a &= -36 \\ a &= \mathbf{-12} \end{aligned}$$

3.1.4 The Magnitude of a Vector

The size or length of a vector $\boldsymbol{u}$ is called its **magnitude** and is written $|\boldsymbol{u}|$.

> If $\boldsymbol{u} = \begin{pmatrix} x \\ y \\ z \end{pmatrix}$, then $|\boldsymbol{u}| = \sqrt{x^2 + y^2 + z^2}$.

The corresponding result for 2 dimensions is:

> If $\boldsymbol{u} = \begin{pmatrix} x \\ y \end{pmatrix}$, then $|\boldsymbol{u}| = \sqrt{x^2 + y^2}$.

Example: If $u = \begin{pmatrix} t \\ 4 \\ -3 \end{pmatrix}$, and $|u| = \sqrt{34}$, find the possible values of t.

$$|u| = \sqrt{34}$$
$$\sqrt{t^2 + 4^2 + (-3)^2} = \sqrt{34}$$
$$t^2 + 16 + 9 = 34$$
$$t^2 - 9 = 0$$

$$(t-3)(t+3) = 0$$
$$t - 3 = 0 \quad \text{or} \quad t + 3 = 0$$
$$\mathbf{t = 3} \qquad \mathbf{t = -3}$$

3.1.5 Position Vectors

Vectors can be used very effectively when working with coordinate geometry.

The vector from the origin of the coordinate system, O, to the point A is called the **position vector** of the point A, and is written:

$$a = \overrightarrow{OA}$$

Note: A position vector cannot be represented by any directed line segment of the same size and direction like other vectors. It is "tied" to starting at the origin.

$$\mathbf{A} = (x, y, z) \text{ if and only if } a = \begin{pmatrix} x \\ y \\ z \end{pmatrix}$$

The Vector $\overrightarrow{AB}$

The vector $\overrightarrow{AB}$ can be given in terms of the position vectors of points A and B.

$$\overrightarrow{AB} = b - a$$

Note: $\overrightarrow{AB}$ is not a position vector.

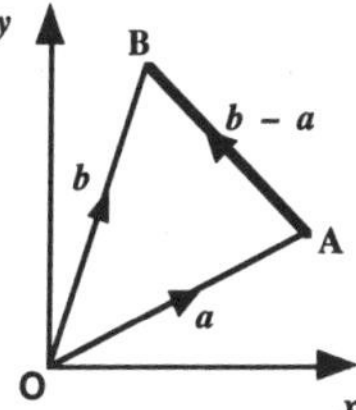

Example: ABCD is a parallelogram. A is the point (–2,3,–1), B is (6,–1,0) and C is (4,2,–5). Find the coordinates of D.

Since ABCD is a parallelogram,

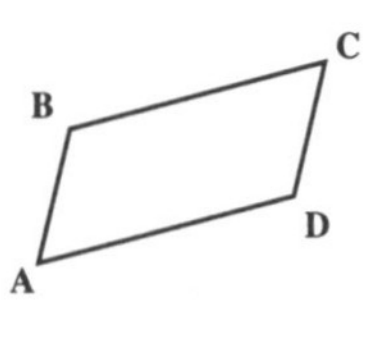

$$\overrightarrow{AB} = \overrightarrow{DC}$$

$$\boldsymbol{b} - \boldsymbol{a} = \boldsymbol{c} - \boldsymbol{d}$$

$$\boldsymbol{d} = \boldsymbol{c} - \boldsymbol{b} + \boldsymbol{a}$$

$$= \begin{pmatrix} 4 \\ 2 \\ -5 \end{pmatrix} - \begin{pmatrix} 6 \\ -1 \\ 0 \end{pmatrix} + \begin{pmatrix} -2 \\ 3 \\ -1 \end{pmatrix}$$

$$= \begin{pmatrix} -4 \\ 6 \\ -6 \end{pmatrix}$$

D has coordinates **(–4,6,–6)**.

3.1.6 Parallel Vectors and Collinear Points

$\boldsymbol{u}$ and $\boldsymbol{v}$ are parallel vectors if and only if $\boldsymbol{u} = k\boldsymbol{v}$.

You can use this to show that three points, A, B and C, are collinear.

1. Find $\overrightarrow{AB}$ and $\overrightarrow{BC}$.
2. Show that $\overrightarrow{BC}$ is equal to a multiple of $\overrightarrow{AB}$. This shows the vectors are parallel.
3. Identify a common point. This shows the points are collinear.
   You must make specific mention of the common point to gain the full marks.

Example: A is the point (–2,3,–2), B is (6,–1,0) and C is (18,–7,3).
Show that A, B and C are collinear.

$$\overrightarrow{AB} = \boldsymbol{b} - \boldsymbol{a} = \begin{pmatrix} 6 \\ -1 \\ 0 \end{pmatrix} - \begin{pmatrix} -2 \\ 3 \\ -2 \end{pmatrix} = \begin{pmatrix} 8 \\ -4 \\ 2 \end{pmatrix} \qquad \overrightarrow{BC} = \boldsymbol{c} - \boldsymbol{b} = \begin{pmatrix} 18 \\ -7 \\ 3 \end{pmatrix} - \begin{pmatrix} 6 \\ -1 \\ 0 \end{pmatrix} = \begin{pmatrix} 12 \\ -6 \\ 3 \end{pmatrix} = \frac{3}{2}\begin{pmatrix} 8 \\ -4 \\ 2 \end{pmatrix}$$

$\overrightarrow{BC} = \frac{3}{2}\overrightarrow{AB}$, so $\overrightarrow{AB}$ and $\overrightarrow{BC}$ are parallel.

Since B is a common point, **A, B and C are collinear.**

3.1.7 Finding a Point which Divides a Line in a Given Ratio

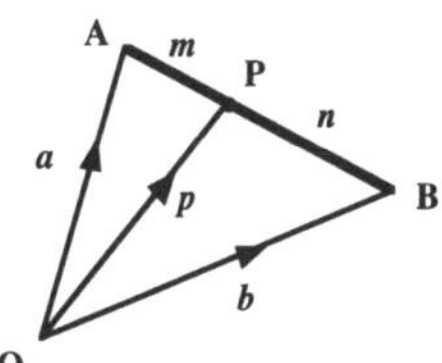

The diagram shows a point P lying on the line AB such that P divides AB in the ratio $m{:}n$.

Problems of this type can be solved using either of the following methods.

Method 1: Giving the position vector $\boldsymbol{p}$ in terms of the position vectors $\boldsymbol{a}$ and $\boldsymbol{b}$.

P is positioned such that $\overrightarrow{AP} = \frac{m}{m+n}\overrightarrow{AB}$,

so
$$\begin{aligned}\boldsymbol{p} &= \overrightarrow{OP}\\ &= \overrightarrow{OA} + \overrightarrow{AP}\\ &= \overrightarrow{OA} + \frac{m}{m+n}\overrightarrow{AB}\\ &= \boldsymbol{a} + \frac{m}{m+n}(\boldsymbol{b}-\boldsymbol{a})\end{aligned}$$

Method 2: Expressing the lengths as a ratio.

P is positioned such that $\frac{AP}{PB} = \frac{m}{n}$,

so
$$\begin{aligned}\frac{AP}{PB} &= \frac{m}{n}\\ n\overrightarrow{AP} &= m\overrightarrow{PB}\\ n(\boldsymbol{p}-\boldsymbol{a}) &= m(\boldsymbol{b}-\boldsymbol{p})\end{aligned}$$

With either method, you should follow the general approach rather than rely on a formula (see Example 1 below).

Example 1: P divides AB in the ratio 2:3.
If A is the point (4,–2,0) and B is (–1,8,–15), find the coordinates of P.

Using Method 1:

$$\boldsymbol{p} = \overrightarrow{OP} = \overrightarrow{OA} + \overrightarrow{AP} = \overrightarrow{OA} + \tfrac{2}{2+3}\overrightarrow{AB}$$

$$\boldsymbol{p} = \boldsymbol{a} + \tfrac{2}{5}(\boldsymbol{b}-\boldsymbol{a})$$

$$= \begin{pmatrix}4\\-2\\0\end{pmatrix} + \frac{2}{5}\left[\begin{pmatrix}-1\\8\\-15\end{pmatrix} - \begin{pmatrix}4\\-2\\0\end{pmatrix}\right]$$

$$= \begin{pmatrix}4\\-2\\0\end{pmatrix} + \frac{2}{5}\begin{pmatrix}-5\\10\\-15\end{pmatrix}$$

$$= \begin{pmatrix}4\\-2\\0\end{pmatrix} + \begin{pmatrix}-2\\4\\-6\end{pmatrix} = \begin{pmatrix}2\\2\\-6\end{pmatrix}$$

P is the point **(2,2,–6)**.

Using Method 2:

$$\begin{aligned}\frac{AP}{PB} &= \frac{2}{3}\\ 3\overrightarrow{AP} &= 2\overrightarrow{PB}\\ 3(\boldsymbol{p}-\boldsymbol{a}) &= 2(\boldsymbol{b}-\boldsymbol{p})\\ 3\boldsymbol{p}-3\boldsymbol{a} &= 2\boldsymbol{b}-2\boldsymbol{p}\\ 5\boldsymbol{p} &= 3\boldsymbol{a}+2\boldsymbol{b}\\ \boldsymbol{p} &= \tfrac{1}{5}(3\boldsymbol{a}+2\boldsymbol{b})\end{aligned}$$

This will lead to the same solution when the position vectors for a and b are substituted in.

Example 2: A is the point $(-1,3,2)$ and B is $(5,0,5)$. C is the point such that $\overrightarrow{AC} = \frac{4}{3}\overrightarrow{AB}$. Find the coordinates of C.

$$\overrightarrow{AC} = \frac{4}{3}\overrightarrow{AB}$$

$$\boldsymbol{c} - \boldsymbol{a} = \frac{4}{3}(\boldsymbol{b} - \boldsymbol{a})$$

$$\boldsymbol{c} - \begin{pmatrix} -1 \\ 3 \\ 2 \end{pmatrix} = \frac{4}{3}\left[\begin{pmatrix} 5 \\ 0 \\ 5 \end{pmatrix} - \begin{pmatrix} -1 \\ 3 \\ 2 \end{pmatrix}\right]$$

$$\boldsymbol{c} = \frac{4}{3}\begin{pmatrix} 6 \\ -3 \\ 3 \end{pmatrix} + \begin{pmatrix} -1 \\ 3 \\ 2 \end{pmatrix} = \begin{pmatrix} 8 \\ -4 \\ 4 \end{pmatrix} + \begin{pmatrix} -1 \\ 3 \\ 2 \end{pmatrix} = \begin{pmatrix} 7 \\ -1 \\ 6 \end{pmatrix}$$

C has coordinates **(7,–1,6)**.

The Section Formula

If a point P divides AB in the ratio $m{:}n$, then:

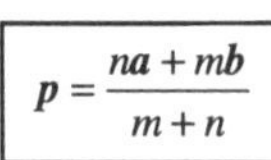

$$p = \frac{na + mb}{m + n}$$

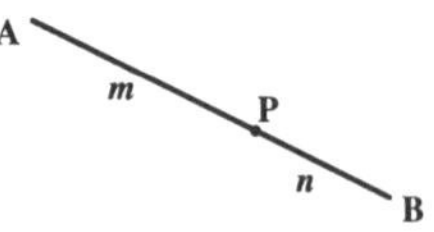

Questions of the above type can also be done using the **Section Formula**. Knowledge of this formula is not required in the Higher syllabus.

3.1.8 Basis Vectors

A vector which has magnitude 1 is called a **unit vector**.

There are three special unit vectors $\boldsymbol{i}, \boldsymbol{j}$ and $\boldsymbol{k}$, which are defined as follows.

$$\boldsymbol{i} = \begin{pmatrix} 1 \\ 0 \\ 0 \end{pmatrix} \quad \boldsymbol{j} = \begin{pmatrix} 0 \\ 1 \\ 0 \end{pmatrix} \quad \boldsymbol{k} = \begin{pmatrix} 0 \\ 0 \\ 1 \end{pmatrix}$$

In 3 dimensions, every other vector can be given as a combination of $\boldsymbol{i}, \boldsymbol{j}$ and $\boldsymbol{k}$. A set of three vectors which has this property is called a **basis** for 3-dimensional space.

Although other vectors can act as a basis, the vectors i, j and k are chosen because they run parallel to the x-axis, y-axis, and z-axis and have unit length. This gives a very simple relationship between component form and the i, j and k form.

$$u = \begin{pmatrix} x \\ y \\ z \end{pmatrix} \text{ if and only if } u = xi + yj + zk$$

Example: $a = -i + 3j + 4k$ and $b = 7i - j + 5k$.
Express $3a - 4b$ in terms of i, j and k.

You can either change into component form and work with components before changing back to the i, j and k form, or work algebraically with the i, j and k form.

Solution using component form:

$$3a - 4b = 3\begin{pmatrix} -1 \\ 3 \\ 4 \end{pmatrix} - 4\begin{pmatrix} 7 \\ -1 \\ 5 \end{pmatrix}$$

$$= \begin{pmatrix} -3 \\ 9 \\ 12 \end{pmatrix} - \begin{pmatrix} 28 \\ -4 \\ 20 \end{pmatrix}$$

$$= \begin{pmatrix} -31 \\ 13 \\ -8 \end{pmatrix}$$

$$= \mathbf{-31i + 13j - 8k}$$

Solution using i, j and k form:

$$3a - 4b$$
$$= 3(-i + 3j + 4k) - 4(7i - j + 5k)$$
$$= -3i + 9j + 12k - 28i + 4j - 20k$$
$$= \mathbf{-31i + 13j - 8k}$$

Similarly in 2 dimensions, the vectors i and j will act as a basis for 2-dimensional space, where:

$$i = \begin{pmatrix} 1 \\ 0 \end{pmatrix} \quad j = \begin{pmatrix} 0 \\ 1 \end{pmatrix}$$

3.1.9 The Scalar Product

The **scalar product** of the vectors $\boldsymbol{a}$ and $\boldsymbol{b}$ is written $\boldsymbol{a}.\boldsymbol{b}$, and is defined to be

$$\boxed{\boldsymbol{a}.\boldsymbol{b} = |\boldsymbol{a}||\boldsymbol{b}|\cos\boldsymbol{\theta}}$$

where θ is the angle between vectors $\boldsymbol{a}$ and $\boldsymbol{b}$, such that $0 \le \theta < \pi$.

The scalar product is often referred to as the **dot product**.
It is a number (scalar) value, <u>not</u> a vector.

The scalar form can also be given in terms of the components of $\boldsymbol{a}$ and $\boldsymbol{b}$.

If $\boldsymbol{a} = \begin{pmatrix} a_1 \\ a_2 \\ a_3 \end{pmatrix}$ and $\boldsymbol{b} = \begin{pmatrix} b_1 \\ b_2 \\ b_3 \end{pmatrix}$, then: $\boxed{\boldsymbol{a}.\boldsymbol{b} = a_1b_1 + a_2b_2 + a_3b_3}$

3.1.10 Using the Scalar Product to Find the Angle Between Vectors

By combining the two forms of the Scalar Product given above, you can find the angle between any two vectors.

If $\boldsymbol{a} = \begin{pmatrix} a_1 \\ a_2 \\ a_3 \end{pmatrix}$ and $\boldsymbol{b} = \begin{pmatrix} b_1 \\ b_2 \\ b_3 \end{pmatrix}$, then $\boldsymbol{a}.\boldsymbol{b} = |\boldsymbol{a}||\boldsymbol{b}|\cos\theta$

and so:

$$\boxed{\cos\boldsymbol{\theta} = \frac{\boldsymbol{a}.\boldsymbol{b}}{|\boldsymbol{a}||\boldsymbol{b}|}}$$

Example 1: $\boldsymbol{a}$ is the vector $\begin{pmatrix} -2 \\ 3 \\ 4 \end{pmatrix}$ and $\boldsymbol{b}$ is the vector $\begin{pmatrix} 1 \\ -3 \\ 5 \end{pmatrix}$.

Find the size of angle between vectors $\boldsymbol{a}$ and $\boldsymbol{b}$.

$|a| = \sqrt{(-2)^2 + 3^2 + 4^2} = \sqrt{29}$

$|b| = \sqrt{1^2 + (-3)^2 + 5^2} = \sqrt{35}$

$$\begin{aligned}\cos\theta &= \frac{a.b}{|a||b|} \\ &= \frac{(-2)\times 1 + 3\times(-3) + 4\times 5}{\sqrt{29}\sqrt{35}} \\ &= 0.282... \\ \theta &= \cos^{-1} 0.282... \\ &= 73.59...\end{aligned}$$

The angle between vectors a and b is **73.6°** to 1 dp.

Often you will be given the coordinates of three points, P, Q and R, and be asked to find the angle between, for example, PQ and QR. In this case you must first set up the required vectors before using the scalar product.

Example 2: P is the point (4,1,0), Q is the point (2,–2,1) and R is the point (–1,–5,2). Find the size of angle PQR.

Use a sketch to clarify what you are looking for.

The required angle **PQR** *is formed by the vectors* $\overrightarrow{QP}$ *and* $\overrightarrow{QR}$ *as shown.*

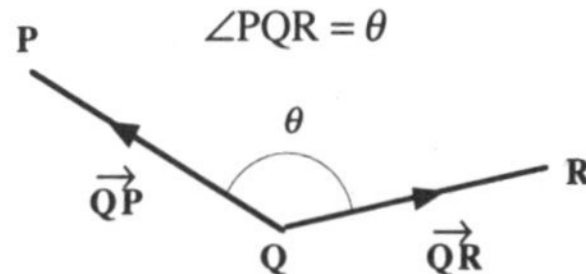

$\overrightarrow{QP} = p - q = \begin{pmatrix}4\\1\\0\end{pmatrix} - \begin{pmatrix}2\\-2\\1\end{pmatrix} = \begin{pmatrix}2\\3\\-1\end{pmatrix}$

$\overrightarrow{QR} = r - q = \begin{pmatrix}-1\\-5\\2\end{pmatrix} - \begin{pmatrix}2\\-2\\1\end{pmatrix} = \begin{pmatrix}-3\\-3\\1\end{pmatrix}$

$|\overrightarrow{QP}| = \sqrt{2^2 + 3^2 + (-1)^2} = \sqrt{14}$

$|\overrightarrow{QR}| = \sqrt{(-3)^2 + (-3)^2 + 1^2} = \sqrt{19}$

$$\begin{aligned}\cos\theta &= \frac{\overrightarrow{QP}.\overrightarrow{QR}}{|\overrightarrow{QP}|\,|\overrightarrow{QR}|} \\ &= \frac{2\times(-3) + 3\times(-3) + (-1)\times 1}{\sqrt{14}\sqrt{19}} \\ &= -0.981...\end{aligned}$$

cosine is negative in 2nd Quadrant

$$\begin{aligned} RA &= \cos^{-1} 0.981... \\ &= 11.17... \\ \theta &= 180 - 11.17... = 168.82... \end{aligned}$$

Angle PQR is **168.8°** to 1 dp.

3.1.11 Using the Scalar Product to Determine Whether Vectors Are Perpendicular

One of the main uses of the Scalar Product is to check whether two vectors are perpendicular.

If $|\boldsymbol{a}| \neq 0$ and $|\boldsymbol{b}| \neq 0$ then, since $\boldsymbol{a}.\boldsymbol{b} = |\boldsymbol{a}||\boldsymbol{b}|\cos\theta$:

$\boldsymbol{a}.\boldsymbol{b} = 0$ if and only if $\boldsymbol{a}$ and $\boldsymbol{b}$ are perpendicular vectors

Example: The vectors $\boldsymbol{u} = \begin{pmatrix} 2 \\ -3 \\ t \end{pmatrix}$ and $\boldsymbol{v} = \begin{pmatrix} -3 \\ t+1 \\ 4 \end{pmatrix}$ are perpendicular.

Find the value of t.

$\boldsymbol{u}$ and $\boldsymbol{v}$ are perpendicular

$$\begin{aligned} \boldsymbol{u}.\boldsymbol{v} &= 0 \\ 2 \times (-3) + (-3) \times (t+1) + t \times 4 &= 0 \\ -6 - 3t - 3 + 4t &= 0 \\ t &= \mathbf{9} \end{aligned}$$

3.1.12 Some Special Results Involving the Scalar Product

$$a \cdot b = b \cdot a$$

The Scalar Product and the Basis Vectors

$$i \cdot i = j \cdot j = k \cdot k = 1$$

$$i \cdot j = j \cdot i = i \cdot k = k \cdot i = j \cdot k = k \cdot j = 0$$

The Scalar Product with Brackets

$$\boxed{a \cdot (b + c) = a \cdot b + a \cdot c}$$

Example: PQR is an equilateral triangle of side 4 units.

$\overrightarrow{PQ} = a$, $\overrightarrow{PR} = b$ and $\overrightarrow{QR} = c$.

Evaluate $a \cdot (b + c)$ and hence identify two vectors which are perpendicular.

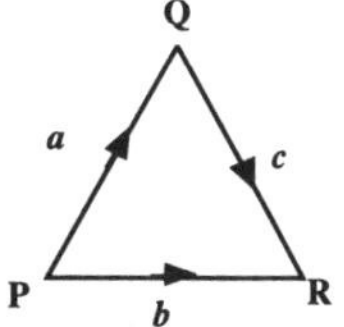

$$\begin{aligned} a.(b+c) &= a.b + a.c \\ &= |a||b|\cos 60^\circ + |a||c|\cos 120^\circ \\ &= 4 \times 4 \times \tfrac{1}{2} + 4 \times 4 \times \left(-\tfrac{1}{2}\right) \\ &= 0 \end{aligned}$$

Note: The angle between a and c is 120°. You must consider the directions as if the two vectors are leaving the same point.

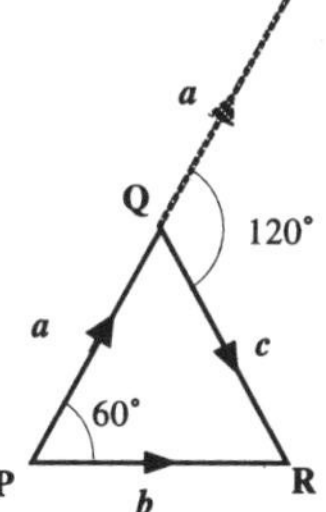

Since $a \cdot (b + c) = 0$, the vectors a and $b + c$ are perpendicular.

3.2 FURTHER DIFFERENTIATION AND INTEGRATION

This section extends the range of functions which can be differentiated or integrated.

These functions could arise in the same types of examples as you met in Section 1.3 (Basic Differentiation) or Section 2.2 (Basic Integration).

3.2.1 The Chain Rule for Differentiation

The basic differentiation rules in Section 1.3.3 allow you to differentiate only sums or differences of simple powers of x.

The **Chain Rule** will allow you to differentiate composite functions.

If $f(x) = g(h(x))$, then $f'(x) = g'((h(x)).h'(x)$.

This can also be written in the form: $\dfrac{dy}{dx} = \dfrac{dy}{du} \cdot \dfrac{du}{dx}$

Example 1:

$$f(x) = (2x+5)^3$$

It may help to think of the f(x) function in terms of g and h as above, and identify g(x) and h(x) separately.

$$x \xrightarrow{h} 2x+5 \xrightarrow{g} (\ \ )^3$$

$$h(x) = 2x+5 \qquad g(x) = x^3$$

$$h'(x) = 2 \qquad g'(x) = 3x^2$$

$$f'(x) = 3(2x+5)^2.2$$
$$= \mathbf{6(2x+5)^2}$$

Example 2:

$$f(x) = (x^2 - 3x)^6$$
$$f'(x) = 6(x^2 - 3x)^5.(2x - 3)$$
$$= \mathbf{6(2x - 3)(x^2 - 3x)^5}$$

Example 3:

$$f(x) = \frac{8}{\sqrt{2x-3}}$$
$$= 8(2x-3)^{-\frac{1}{2}}$$
$$f'(x) = 8 \times \left(-\tfrac{1}{2}\right)(2x-3)^{-\frac{3}{2}} \times 2$$
$$= \frac{\mathbf{-8}}{\mathbf{(2x-3)^{\frac{3}{2}}}}$$

3.2.2 Differentiation of Trig Functions

The basic rules for differentiating trig functions are:

$f(x) = \sin x$	$\rightarrow$	$f'(x) = \cos x$
$f(x) = \cos x$	$\rightarrow$	$f'(x) = -\sin x$

The Chain Rule can be used to extend these to:

$f(x) = \sin(ax + b)$	$\rightarrow$	$f'(x) = a\cos(ax + b)$
$f(x) = \cos(ax + b)$	$\rightarrow$	$f'(x) = -a\sin(ax + b)$

Example 1:

$$f(x) = \sin 3x$$
$$f'(x) = \mathbf{3\cos 3x}$$

Example 2:

$$f(x) = 5\cos(2x + \tfrac{\pi}{2})$$
$$f'(x) = 5 \times (-2)\sin(2x + \tfrac{\pi}{2})$$
$$= \mathbf{-10\sin(2x + \tfrac{\pi}{2})}$$

More complicated functions can be differentiated using the Chain Rule as in Section 3.2.1. Again, it may help to break the function up into the component parts.

Example 3:

$f(x) = \sin(x^2 - 3)$

$x \xrightarrow{h} x^2 - 3 \xrightarrow{g} \sin(\ \ )$

$h(x) = x^2 - 3 \qquad g(x) = \sin x$

$h'(x) = 2x \qquad g'(x) = \cos x$

$$\begin{aligned} f'(x) &= \cos(x^2 - 3).2x \\ &= \mathbf{2x\cos(x^2 - 3)} \end{aligned}$$

Example 4:

$f(x) = 3\cos^2 x$

Note: $3\cos^2 x = 3(\cos x)^2$

$x \xrightarrow{h} \cos x \xrightarrow{g} 3(\ \ )^2$

$h(x) = \cos x \qquad g(x) = 3x^2$

$h'(x) = -\sin x \qquad g'(x) = 6x$

$$\begin{aligned} f'(x) &= 6\cos x.(-\sin x) \\ &= \mathbf{-6\cos x\ \sin x} \end{aligned}$$

3.2.3 Integrating $f(x) = (ax+b)^n$

There is no integration rule equivalent to the chain rule for differentiation.

The following rule will allow you to integrate powers of $ax + b$, but it cannot be extended to other functions.

$$\int (ax+b)^n\,dx = \frac{(ax+b)^{n+1}}{a(n+1)} + C \qquad (n \neq -1)$$

Example 1:

$$\begin{aligned} &\int (2x-3)^5\,dx \\ &= \frac{(2x-3)^6}{2\times 6} + C \\ &= \tfrac{1}{12}(2x-3)^6 + C \end{aligned}$$

Example 2:

$$\begin{aligned} &\int \frac{1}{\sqrt{x+1}}\,dx \\ &= \int (x+1)^{-\frac{1}{2}}\,dx \\ &= \frac{(x+1)^{\frac{1}{2}}}{1\times\frac{1}{2}} + C \\ &= 2(x+1)^{\frac{1}{2}} + C \end{aligned}$$

or

$$= 2\sqrt{x+1} + C$$

Example 3:

$$\int_{-1}^{0}(3x+2)^3\,dx$$

$$=\left[\frac{(3x+2)^4}{3\times 4}\right]_{-1}^{0}$$

$$=\left[\frac{(3x+2)^4}{12}\right]_{-1}^{0}$$

$$=\left(\frac{(3\times 0+2)^4}{12}\right)-\left(\frac{(3\times(-1)+2)^4}{12}\right)$$

$$=\frac{2^4}{12}-\frac{(-1)^4}{12}$$

$$=\frac{16}{12}-\frac{1}{12}$$

$$=\frac{15}{12}=\mathbf{\frac{5}{4}}$$

3.2.4 Integrating Trig Functions

The basic rules for integrating trig functions are:

$$\int\cos x\,dx=\sin x+C \qquad \int\sin x\,dx=-\cos x+C$$

These can be extended to:

$$\int\cos(ax+b)dx=\frac{1}{a}\sin(ax+b)+C$$

$$\int\sin(ax+b)dx=-\frac{1}{a}\cos(ax+b)+C$$

Example 1:

$$\int \cos(2x-1)\,dx$$
$$= \tfrac{1}{2}\sin(2x-1)+C$$

Example 2:

$$\int 2\sin(3-x)\,dx$$
$$= 2\times\tfrac{1}{-1}(-\cos(3-x))+C$$
$$= 2\cos(3-x)+C$$

Example 3: (a) Evaluate $\int_0^{\pi}\cos 2x\,dx$.

(b) Draw a sketch and explain your answer.

(a)

$$\int_0^{\pi}\cos 2x\,dx = \left[\tfrac{1}{2}\sin 2x\right]_0^{\pi}$$
$$= \left(\tfrac{1}{2}\sin(2\times\pi)\right)-\left(\tfrac{1}{2}\sin(2\times 0)\right)$$
$$= 0-0=\mathbf{0}$$

(b)

***y* = cos 2*x* is a cos-shaped graph with a period of π, as shown.**

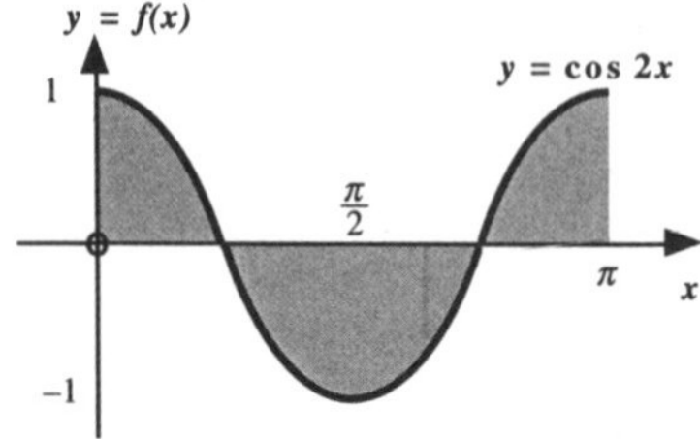

$\int_0^{\pi}\cos 2x\,dx$ gives the area between the curve $y=\cos 2x$ and the x-axis from 0 to π.

The total area of the two parts above the x-axis is equal to the area of the part below the x-axis.
The integrals will have different signs and cancel out to give the value **0**.

3.3 LOGARITHMIC AND EXPONENTIAL FUNCTIONS

3.3.1 Exponential and Logarithmic Functions

Exponential and logarithmic functions were defined in Section 1.2.19 and Section 1.2.20 and their graphs were considered there.

The function $f(x) = a^x$, $a > 0$, is called **an exponential function**.
a can take different values. In many practical examples in science, you use e (= **2.718...**) for a. e is a very important mathematical constant, like π.

When $a = e, f(x) = e^x$ is called **the exponential function**.

Most calculators have special buttons for 10^x and e^x. Other values for a can be calculated using the power button.

The function $f(x) = \log_a x$, $a > 0$, is called a **logarithmic function**.
a is called the **base**.

When $a = e$, $\log_e x$ is called the **natural logarithmic function**. This is often written as $\ln x$, and appears in this form on most calculators.

On most calculators, $\log x$ is used to mean $a = 10$, ie $\log_{10} x$.
There is no log button on most calculators for other base values.

Some of the results using logarithms will true for any base value a. In these cases, $\log_a x$ will often be written as $\log x$.

Each logarithmic function is the inverse of the corresponding exponential function.

This gives the basic result:

$$y = a^x \quad \text{if and only if} \quad x = \log_a y \quad (a > 1,\ x > 0)$$

It can be helpful to make use of a diagram like the one below to convert from an exponential statement to a logarithmic statement. See the following examples.

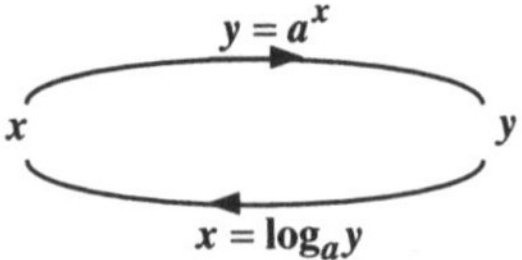

Example 1: $A = 350e^{0.5t}$.
Find the value of (a) A when $t = 10$ and (b) t when $A = 3500$, giving each value correct to 3 significant figures.

(a) $A = 350e^{0.5t}$

$= 350e^{0.5\times 10}$

$= 51944.6...$

$=$ **51900** to 3 sf

(b) $3500 = 350e^{0.5t}$

$\frac{3500}{350} = e^{0.5t}$

$10 = e^{0.5t}$ ◄——

$0.5t = \log_e 10$

$t = \frac{\log_e 10}{0.5}$

$= 4.605...$

$=$ **4.61** to 3 sf

$e^{0.5t}$

$0.5t$ — 10

$\log_e 10$

Example 2: The chemical Alisonium decays according to the rule $m = m_0 e^{-0.03t}$, where m is the mass in grams at time t in years, and m_0 is the original mass. The **half-life** is the time taken for half of the mass to decay. Find the half-life of Alisonium.

***Note the use of* $\ln x$ *as an alternative notation to* $\log_e x$.**

$m = m_0 e^{-0.03t}$ At half-life $m = \frac{1}{2}m_0$

$\frac{1}{2}m_0 = m_0 e^{-0.03t}$

$\frac{1}{2} = e^{-0.03t}$ ◄——

$\ln\frac{1}{2} = -0.03t$

$t = \frac{\ln\frac{1}{2}}{-0.03}$

$= 23.10...$

$= 23.1$ to 1dp Alisonium has a half-life of **23.1** years.

$e^{-0.03t}$

$-0.03t$ — $\frac{1}{2}$

$\ln\frac{1}{2}$

3.3.2 The Log Rules

For any base a:

$$\log_a 1 = 0 \qquad \log_a a = 1$$

For any base:

$$\log AB = \log A + \log B \qquad \log \frac{A}{B} = \log A - \log B$$

$$\log A^n = n \log A$$

These rules can be used to simplify logarithmic expressions.

Example:

$$\begin{aligned} &5\log_8 2 + \log_8 4 - \log_8 16 \\ &= \log_8 2^5 + \log_8 4 - \log_8 16 \\ &= \log_8 \frac{2^5 \times 4}{16} \\ &= \log_8 8 \\ &= \mathbf{1} \end{aligned}$$

3.3.3 Solving Simple Exponential and Logarithmic Equations

Simple examples can be solved using the basic result from Section 3.3.1. Solutions can be left as exact values, as in Example 1, or as approximate values, as in Example 2.

Example 1:

$$\begin{aligned} 10^{x+1} &= 5 \\ x+1 &= \log_{10} 5 \\ x &= \mathbf{\log_{10} 5 - 1} \end{aligned}$$

Example 2:

$$\begin{aligned} \ln(x-3) &= 2.5 \\ x-3 &= e^{2.5} \\ x &= e^{2.5} + 3 \\ &= \mathbf{15.2} \quad \text{to 1 dp} \end{aligned}$$

Equations may arise in the context of a graph.

Example 3: Part of the graph of $y = 5\log_{10}(4x + 6)$ is shown in the diagram below. This graph cuts the x-axis at the point A and the straight line $y = 7$ at the point B. Find algebraically the x-coordinates of A and B.

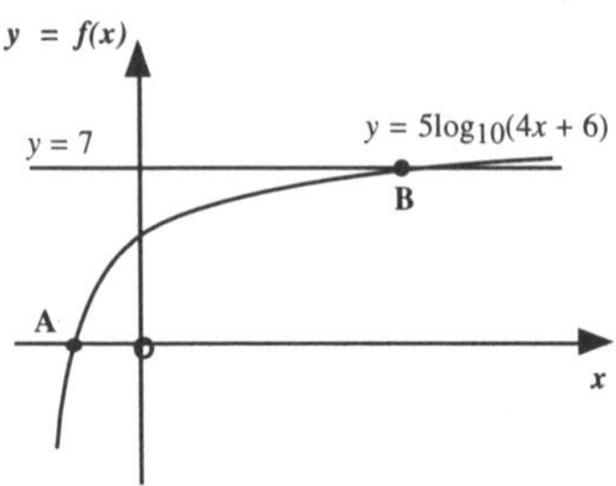

At point A on the curve, $y = 0$

$$0 = 5\log_{10}(4x+6)$$
$$\log_{10}(4x+6) = 0$$
$$4x+6 = 1 \leftarrow (\log_a 1 = 0)$$
$$4x = -5$$
$$x = -1.25$$

A has an x-coordinate **−1.25**.

At point B on the curve, $y = 7$

$$7 = 5\log_{10}(4x+6)$$
$$5\log_{10}(4x+6) = 7$$
$$\log_{10}(4x+6) = \tfrac{7}{5} = 1.4$$
$$4x+6 = 10^{1.4}$$
$$4x = 10^{1.4} - 6$$
$$x = \frac{10^{1.4} - 6}{4}$$
$$= 4.77...$$

B has an x-coordinate **4.8**.

3.3.4 Exponential Equations of the Form $a^x = b$ ($a \neq e$ or 10)

Equations of this form cannot be undone using the equivalent logarithmic function as you cannot in general evaluate logs with bases other than e or 10.

1. Rearrange the equation to obtain the form $a^x = b$.
2. Take the log of both sides using either base e or base 10.
3. Use the log rule to bring the x term out of the power.
4. Solve the resulting equation.

Example 1:

$$
\begin{aligned}
5^x &= 65 \\
\log_{10} 5^x &= \log_{10} 65 \\
x \log_{10} 5 &= \log_{10} 65 \\
x &= \frac{\log_{10} 65}{\log_{10} 5} \\
&= \mathbf{2.59} \quad \text{to 3 sf}
\end{aligned}
$$

Example 2:

$$
\begin{aligned}
2.5^{x+1} &= 150 \\
\ln 2.5^{x+1} &= \ln 150 \\
(x+1)\ln 2.5 &= \ln 150 \\
x+1 &= \frac{\ln 150}{\ln 2.5} \\
x &= \frac{\ln 150}{\ln 2.5} - 1 \\
&= \mathbf{4.47} \quad \text{to 3 sf}
\end{aligned}
$$

3.3.5 Polynomial Relationships of the Form $y = ax^b$

A relationship of this form would produce a polynomial curve. It is not easy, given a graph of this type, to find the values of a and b.

You can make use of the logarithmic functions to transform a relationship of this type into an equivalent linear relationship, as shown below. It is much easier to find the values of a and b from the straight line graph obtained.

1. Transform the polynomial relationship into the equivalent linear relationship using the following method. You can use either base e or base 10 logarithms.

$$
\begin{aligned}
y &= ax^b \\
\log y &= \log ax^b \\
\log y &= \log a + \log x^b \\
\log y &= \log a + b \log x \\
\mathbf{\log y} &= b\,\mathbf{\log x} + \log a
\end{aligned}
$$

   This gives a linear relationship between the $\mathbf{\log y}$ values and the $\mathbf{\log x}$ values.

2. Plot the $\log y$ values against the $\log x$ values. You will obtain a straight line with gradient b which cuts the y-axis at $\log a$.
   (In an exam question, the graph will often be given to you as in the example below.)

3. Choose any two points on the line, and use them to find the gradient, ie the value of b.

4. Either read the y-axis intercept from the graph or work it out algebraically (see the example). This will give the value of $\log a$. You can then obtain the value of a.

Example: The graph shows the relationship between Y (=$\log_{10}y$) and X (=$\log_{10}x$).

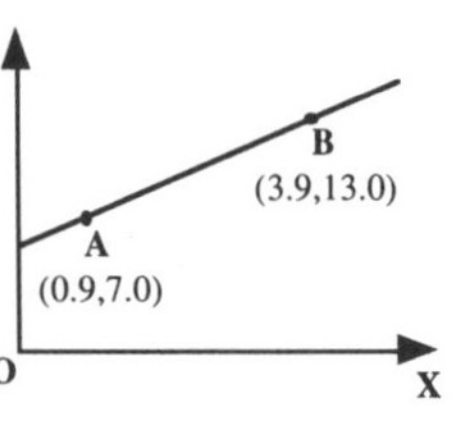

Find the equation of the line in the form $Y = mX + c$.

If there is a relationship between x and y of the form $y = ax^b$, find the values of a and b.

$$m_{AB} = \frac{y_2 - y_1}{x_2 - x_1} = \frac{13.0 - 7.0}{3.9 - 0.9} = \frac{6}{3} = 2$$

The line has equation of the form $Y = mX + c$, so

$$Y = 2X + c$$

(0.9,7.0) is a point on the line, so

$$7.0 = 2 \times 0.9 + c$$
$$c = 7.0 - 1.8 = 5.2$$

The line has equation $\mathbf{Y = 2X + 5.2}$

$$y = ax^b$$
$$\log_{10} y = \log_{10} ax^b$$
$$\log_{10} y = \log_{10} a + \log_{10} x^b$$
$$\log_{10} y = \log_{10} a + b\log_{10} x$$
$$\log_{10} y = b\log_{10} x + \log_{10} a$$

$$Y = bX + \log_{10} a$$

and $Y = 2X + 5.2$

$$b = \mathbf{2}$$

$$\log_{10} a = 5.2$$
$$a = 10^{5.2}$$
$$= \mathbf{158000} \text{ to 3 sf}$$

3.3.6 Exponential Relationships of the Form $y = ab^x$

A similar approach can be used with exponential relationships to identify the values of a and b.

1. Transform the exponential relationship into the equivalent linear relationship using the following method. You can use either base e or base 10 logarithms.

$$y = ab^x$$
$$\log y = \log ab^x$$
$$\log y = \log a + \log b^x$$
$$\log y = \log a + x \log b$$
$$\mathbf{\log y} = \log b.\boldsymbol{x} + \log a$$

   This gives a linear relationship between the $\mathbf{\log y}$ values and the $\boldsymbol{x}$ values.

2. Plot the $\log y$ values against the x values. You will obtain a straight line with gradient $\log b$ which cuts the y-axis at $\log a$.

3. Choose any two points on the line, and use them to find the gradient, ie the value of $\log b$. You can then obtain the value of b.

4. Either read the y-axis intercept from the graph or work it out algebraically (see the example below). This will give the value of $\log a$. You can then obtain the value of a.

You will often be told the relationship is polynomial of the type $y = ax^b$, but you could also be asked to confirm this, as in the example below.

Example: Values for x and y were recorded during an experiment.

x	2.2	3.3	3.9	4.5
y	17.2	101	266	699

It is thought that x and y are connected by a relationship of the form $y = ab^x$.

By drawing a graph of Y (= $\log_e y$) against x, confirm that this is case and find values for a and b.

$$y = ab^x$$
$$\log_e y = \log_e ab^x$$
$$\log_e y = \log_e a + \log_e b^x$$
$$\log_e y = \log_e a + x\log_e b$$
$$\log_e y = \log_e b.x + \log_e a$$

which is in the form

$$Y = mx + c$$

where $Y = \log_e y$

Find the values of $Y = \log_e y$ and plot these against x.

x	2.2	3.3	3.9	4.5
$Y = ln\ y$	2.84	4.62	5.58	6.55

Draw the line of best fit through the points.

Since the graph of $Y (= \log_e y)$ against x gives a straight line, this confirms **the relationship has the form $y = ab^x$.**

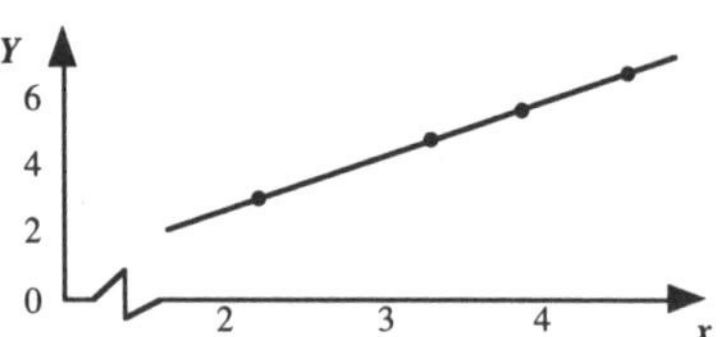

Since the first and last points lie on the line, use them to find the equation of the line.

$$m = \frac{6.55 - 2.84}{4.5 - 2.2}$$
$$= \frac{3.71}{2.3}$$
$$= 1.61...$$

The line has equation of the form $Y = mx + c$, so

$$Y = 1.61... \times x + c$$

$(2.2, 2.84)$ is a point on the line, so

$$2.84 = 1.61... \times 2.2 + c$$
$$c = 2.84 - 3.54... = -0.70...$$

The line has equation $Y = 1.61...x - 0.70...$

$$\log_e b = 1.61...$$
$$b = e^{1.61...}$$
$$= \mathbf{5.0} \quad \text{to 1 dp}$$

$$\log_e a = -0.70...$$
$$a = e^{-0.70...}$$
$$= \mathbf{0.5} \quad \text{to 1 dp}$$

The relationship is $\mathbf{y = 0.5 \times 5.0^x}$

3.4 FURTHER TRIGONOMETRIC RELATIONSHIPS

3.4.1 $a\cos\theta + b\sin\theta$

Any expression of the form $a\cos\theta + b\sin\theta$ can be expressed in one of the following forms.

$r\cos(\theta + \alpha)$	$r\cos(\theta - \alpha)$
$r\sin(\theta + \alpha)$	$r\sin(\theta - \alpha)$

1. Choose which of the forms you wish to use. (Some questions will specify a particular form, and in that case you must use the one specified.)
2. Use the appropriate addition formula to expand the chosen form.
3. Equate the coefficients of $\cos\theta$ and $\sin\theta$, remembering to include any negative signs, to give you two equations in r and α. Label them **(1)** and **(2)**.
4. Solve these equations, making use of the basic trig identity $\cos^2\alpha + \sin^2\alpha = 1$, as shown in the examples below, to find the value of r.

   You will always square the two equations and add them together.
   You always take r as positive.
5. Solve the equations, making use of the basic trig identity $\tan\alpha = \dfrac{\sin\alpha}{\cos\alpha}$, as shown in the examples below, to find the value of α.

   You will always divide the sine equation by the cosine equation to obtain the tangent statement. In some cases, this will involve dividing equation **(1)** by equation **(2)**, and in others equation **(2)** by equation **(1)**.

   You must check which quadrant α is in by checking whether each of sine, cosine and tangent is positive or negative.

The examples below illustrate the method. You must show the working each time. It is not sufficient to use a formula to obtain r and α.

The same approach is used for degrees (see Example 1 below) and radians (see Example 2 below). Values for r and α may be given as exact values or as numerical approximations, as appropriate.

Example 1: Express $3\cos x^\circ + 4\sin x^\circ$ in the form $r\cos(x-\alpha)^\circ$.

$$\begin{aligned}3\cos x^\circ + 4\sin x^\circ &= r\cos(x-\alpha)^\circ\\ &= r(\cos x^\circ\cos\alpha^\circ + \sin x^\circ\sin\alpha^\circ)\\ &= r\cos x^\circ\cos\alpha^\circ + r\sin x^\circ\sin\alpha^\circ\\ 3\underline{\cos x^\circ} + 4\underline{\underline{\sin x^\circ}} &= r\cos\alpha^\circ\underline{\cos x^\circ} + r\sin\alpha^\circ\underline{\underline{\sin x^\circ}}\end{aligned}$$

It can be helpful to underline the $\cos x$ and $\sin x$ on each side to help identify the corresponding coefficients.

$3 = r\cos\alpha^\circ$ **(1)** $\qquad 4 = r\sin\alpha^\circ$ **(2)**

Using $(1)^2 + (2)^2$

$$\begin{aligned}3^2 + 4^2 &= r^2\cos^2\alpha^\circ + r^2\sin^2\alpha^\circ\\ 25 &= r^2\\ r &= 5\end{aligned}$$

Using $\dfrac{(2)}{(1)}$

$$\frac{4}{3} = \frac{r\sin\alpha^\circ}{r\cos\alpha^\circ} = \tan\alpha^\circ$$

$\tan\alpha^\circ = 1.333...$

$RA = \tan^{-1}1.333... = 53.13...^\circ$

$\sin, \cos, \tan$ are all positive $\rightarrow$ 1st Quadrant

$\alpha = 53.1$ to 1 dp

$$3\cos x^\circ + 4\sin x^\circ = \mathbf{5\cos(x - 53.1)^\circ}$$

Example 2: Express $\sin\theta + \cos\theta$ in the form $r\sin(\theta - \alpha)$.

$$\begin{aligned}\sin\theta + \cos\theta &= r\sin(\theta-\alpha)\\ &= r(\sin\theta\cos\alpha - \cos\theta\sin\alpha)\\ &= r\sin\theta\cos\alpha - r\cos\theta\sin\alpha\\ \underline{\underline{\sin\theta}} + \underline{\cos\theta} &= r\cos\alpha\underline{\underline{\sin\theta}} - r\sin\alpha\underline{\cos\theta}\end{aligned}$$

$1 = -r\sin\alpha$ $\qquad 1 = r\cos\alpha$ **(2)**

$-1 = r\sin\alpha$ **(1)**

Using $(1)^2 + (2)^2$

$$(-1)^2 + 1^2 = r^2 \sin^2 \alpha + r^2 \cos^2 \alpha$$
$$2 = r^2$$
$$r = \sqrt{2}$$

Using $\frac{(1)}{(2)}$

$$\frac{-1}{1} = \frac{r \sin \alpha}{r \cos \alpha} = \tan \alpha$$
$$\tan \alpha = -1$$
$$RA = \tan^{-1} 1 = \tfrac{\pi}{4}$$

cos is positive;

sin, tan are negative $\rightarrow$ 4th Quadrant

$$\alpha = 2\pi - \tfrac{\pi}{4} = \tfrac{7\pi}{4}$$

$$\sin\theta + \cos\theta = \boldsymbol{\sqrt{2}\sin(\theta - \tfrac{7\pi}{4})}$$

3.4.2 The Maximum and Minimum Values of $a \cos\theta + b \sin\theta$

When an expression is in the form $\boldsymbol{a \cos\theta + b \sin\theta}$ is not easy to identify its maximum or minimum.

When this expression is given in the form $\boldsymbol{r \cos}\ (\theta \pm \alpha)$ or $\boldsymbol{r \sin}\ (\theta \pm \alpha)$, you can use the methods of Section 1.2.18 to identify the maximum or minimum value and where it occurs.

Example: Express $f(x) = 5\cos x^\circ + 2\sin x^\circ$ in the form $r\sin(x + \alpha)^\circ$, and hence find its maximum value and the value of x where it occurs, $0 \le x < 360$.

$$5\cos x^\circ + 2\sin x^\circ = r\sin(x+\alpha)^\circ$$
$$= r(\sin x^\circ \cos\alpha^\circ + \cos x^\circ \sin\alpha^\circ)$$
$$= r\sin x^\circ \cos\alpha^\circ + r\cos x^\circ \sin\alpha^\circ$$
$$5\underline{\cos x^\circ} + 2\underline{\underline{\sin x^\circ}} = r\cos\alpha^\circ \underline{\underline{\sin x^\circ}} + r\sin\alpha^\circ \underline{\cos x^\circ}$$

$$5 = r\sin\alpha^\circ \quad \textbf{(1)} \qquad 2 = r\cos\alpha^\circ \quad \textbf{(2)}$$

Using $(1)^2 + (2)^2$

$$5^2 + 2^2 = r^2 \sin^2 \alpha° + r^2 \cos^2 \alpha°$$
$$29 = r^2$$
$$r = \sqrt{29}$$

Using $\frac{(1)}{(2)}$

$$\frac{5}{2} = \frac{r \sin \alpha°}{r \cos \alpha°} = \tan \alpha°$$
$$\tan \alpha° = 2.5$$
$$RA = \tan^{-1} 2.5 = 68.19...°$$

$\sin, \cos, \tan$ are all positive $\rightarrow$ 1st Quadrant

$\alpha = 68.2$ to 1 dp

$f(x) = 5 \cos x° + 2 \sin x° = \sqrt{29} \sin (x + 68.2)°$

$f(x)$ has a maximum value of **√29**, when

$$x + 68.2 = 90$$ ◄——— **sin *takes its maximum at* 90°.**

$$x = 21.8$$

3.4.3 The Maximum and Minimum Values of $a \cos\theta + b \sin\theta + c$

For an expression of the form $a \cos\theta + b \sin\theta + c$, change $a \cos\theta + b \sin\theta$ into the form $r \cos (\theta \pm \alpha)$ or $r \sin (\theta \pm \alpha)$ as above.

Example: Find the minimum value of $f(x) = \sin\theta + \cos\theta + 4$ and the value of x where it occurs, $0 \leq \theta < 2\pi$.

From Example 2 in Section 3.4.1 above

$$\sin\theta + \cos\theta = \sqrt{2} \sin\left(\theta - \tfrac{7\pi}{4}\right)$$
$$\sin\theta + \cos\theta + 4 = \sqrt{2} \sin\left(\theta - \tfrac{7\pi}{4}\right) + 4$$

$f(x) = \sin\theta + \cos\theta + 4$ has a minimum value of $-\sqrt{2} + 4$, when

$$\theta - \tfrac{7\pi}{4} = \tfrac{3\pi}{2}$$ ◄——— **sin *takes its minimum at* $\frac{3\pi}{2}$.**

$$\theta = \tfrac{3\pi}{2} + \tfrac{7\pi}{4}$$
$$= \tfrac{13\pi}{4}$$

This value is outside the required domain, so subtract 2π.

$$\theta = \tfrac{13\pi}{4} - 2\pi = \tfrac{5\pi}{4}$$

3.4.4 Solving Trig Equations of the Form $a\cos\theta + b\sin\theta = c$

Change $a\cos\theta + b\sin\theta$ into the form $r\cos(\theta \pm \alpha)$ or $r\sin(\theta \pm \alpha)$ as above, and then solve as in Section 2.3.7. Some rearranging may be required first.

Example: Express $\sqrt{3}\cos\theta - \sin\theta$ in the form $r\cos(\theta + \alpha)$, and hence solve the equation $\sqrt{3}\cos\theta - \sin\theta - \sqrt{3} = 0$ where $0 \le \theta < 2\pi$.

$$\begin{aligned}\sqrt{3}\cos\theta - \sin\theta &= r\cos(\theta+\alpha)\\ &= r(\cos\theta\cos\alpha - \sin\theta\sin\alpha)\\ &= r\cos\theta\cos\alpha - r\sin\theta\sin\alpha\end{aligned}$$

$$\sqrt{3}\underline{\cos\theta} - \underline{\underline{\sin\theta}} = r\cos\alpha\underline{\cos\theta} - r\sin\alpha\underline{\underline{\sin\theta}}$$

$$\sqrt{3} = r\cos\alpha \quad \textbf{(1)}$$

$$-1 = -r\sin\alpha$$
$$1 = r\sin\alpha \quad \textbf{(2)}$$

Using $\textbf{(1)}^2 + \textbf{(2)}^2$

$$\left(\sqrt{3}\right)^2 + 1^2 = r^2\cos^2\alpha + r^2\sin^2\alpha$$
$$4 = r^2$$
$$r = 2$$

Using $\frac{\textbf{(2)}}{\textbf{(1)}}$

$$\frac{1}{\sqrt{3}} = \frac{r\sin\alpha}{r\cos\alpha} = \tan\alpha$$
$$\tan\alpha = \tfrac{1}{\sqrt{3}}$$
$$RA = \tan^{-1}\tfrac{1}{\sqrt{3}} = \tfrac{\pi}{6}$$

$\sin, \cos, \tan$ all positive $\rightarrow$ 1st Quadrant

$$\alpha = \tfrac{\pi}{6}$$

$$\sqrt{3}\cos\theta - \sin\theta = \mathbf{2\cos(\boldsymbol{\theta} + \tfrac{\boldsymbol{\pi}}{6})}$$

$$\begin{aligned}\sqrt{3}\cos\theta - \sin\theta - \sqrt{3} &= 0\\ 2\cos\left(\theta + \tfrac{\pi}{6}\right) - \sqrt{3} &= 0\\ 2\cos\left(\theta + \tfrac{\pi}{6}\right) &= \sqrt{3}\\ \cos\left(\theta + \tfrac{\pi}{6}\right) &= \tfrac{\sqrt{3}}{2}\end{aligned}$$

cosine is positive in 1st and 4th Quadrants

$$RA = \cos^{-1}\tfrac{\sqrt{3}}{2}$$
$$= \tfrac{\pi}{6}$$

1st Quadrant: $\theta + \tfrac{\pi}{6} = \tfrac{\pi}{6}$

$$\theta = \tfrac{\pi}{6} - \tfrac{\pi}{6} = 0$$

4th Quadrant: $\theta + \tfrac{\pi}{6} = 2\pi - \tfrac{\pi}{6}$

$$\theta = 2\pi - \tfrac{\pi}{6} - \tfrac{\pi}{6} = \tfrac{5\pi}{3}$$

Solution: $\mathbf{x = 0}$ or $\mathbf{x = \tfrac{5\pi}{3}}$

3.4.5 $a \cos n\theta + b \sin n\theta$

Any expression of the form $a\cos n\theta + b\sin n\theta$ can be expressed in one of the following forms.

$r \cos (n\theta + \alpha)$	$r \cos (n\theta - \alpha)$
$r \sin (n\theta + \alpha)$	$r \sin (n\theta - \alpha)$

This is done using the same approach as in the rest of this section.

See Section 2.3.7 for methods of solving equations invoving compound angles.

Example: Express $4\cos 2x^\circ + 2\sin 2x^\circ$ in the form $r\cos(2x - \alpha)^\circ$, and hence solve the equation $4\cos 2x^\circ + 2\sin 2x^\circ + 2 = 0$ where $0 \le x < 360$.

$$4\cos 2x^\circ + 2\sin 2x^\circ = r\cos(2x - \alpha)^\circ$$
$$= r(\cos 2x^\circ \cos\alpha^\circ + \sin 2x^\circ \sin\alpha^\circ)$$
$$= r\cos 2x^\circ \cos\alpha^\circ + r\sin 2x^\circ \sin\alpha^\circ$$
$$4\underline{\cos 2x^\circ} + 2\underline{\underline{\sin 2x^\circ}} = r\cos\alpha^\circ \underline{\cos 2x^\circ} + r\sin\alpha^\circ \underline{\underline{\sin 2x^\circ}}$$

$$4 = r\cos\alpha^\circ \quad \textbf{(1)} \qquad 2 = r\sin\alpha^\circ \quad \textbf{(2)}$$

Using $(\mathbf{1})^2 + (\mathbf{2})^2$

$$4^2 + 2^2 = r^2 \cos^2 \alpha° + r^2 \sin^2 \alpha°$$

$$20 = r^2$$

$$r = \sqrt{20}$$

Using $\frac{(\mathbf{2})}{(\mathbf{1})}$

$$\frac{2}{4} = \frac{r \sin \alpha°}{r \cos \alpha°} = \tan \alpha°$$

$$\tan \alpha° = 0.5$$

$$RA = \tan^{-1} 0.5 = 26.56...°$$

$\sin, \cos, \tan$ all positive → 1st Quadrant

$$\alpha = 26.56...$$

$$4\cos 2x° + 2\sin 2x° = \mathbf{\sqrt{20}\cos(2x - 26.56...)°}$$

$$4\cos 2x° + 2\sin 2x° + 2 = 0$$

$$\sqrt{20}\cos(2x - 26.56...)° + 2 = 0$$

$$\sqrt{20}\cos(2x - 26.56...)° = -2$$

$$\cos(2x - 26.56...)° = \frac{-2}{\sqrt{20}} = -0.447...$$

cosine is negative in 2nd and 3rd Quadrants, period is 180°

$$RA = \cos^{-1} 0.447...$$

$$= 63.43...°$$

2nd Quadrant: $2x - 26.56... = 180 - 63.43...$

$$2x = 180 - 63.43... + 26.56... = 143.13...$$

$x = 71.56... = 71.6$ to 1 dp

3rd Quadrant: $2x - 26.56... = 180 + 63.43...$

$$2x = 180 + 63.43... + 26.56... = 269.99...$$

$x = 134.99... = 135.0$ to 1 dp

Basic solutions $x = 71.6$ or $x = 135.0$

Add 180° $x = 251.6$ or $x = 315.0$

Add 360° out of specified domain

Solution: $x = \mathbf{71.6}$ or $x = \mathbf{135.0}$ or $x = \mathbf{251.6}$ or $x = \mathbf{315.0}$

Detailed Index A - Z

Detailed Index A - Z